Homework Helpers

Eureka Math
Grade 2

Special thanks go to the Gordan A. Cain Center and to the Department of Mathematics at Louisiana State University for their support in the development of *Eureka Math*.

Homework Helpers

Grade 2
Module 1

G2-M1-Lesson 1

Fluency Practice

Making ten and adding to ten is foundational to future Grade 2 strategies. Students use a number bond to show the part–whole relationship with numbers.

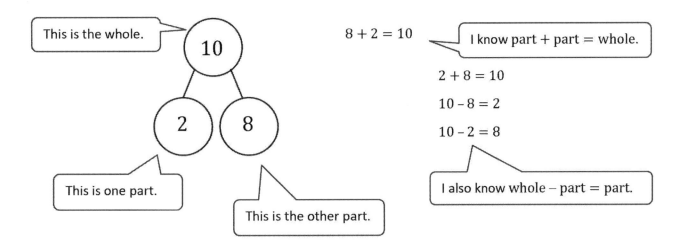

This is the whole.

10

2   8

This is one part.

This is the other part.

$8 + 2 = 10$

I know part + part = whole.

$2 + 8 = 10$

$10 - 8 = 2$

$10 - 2 = 8$

I also know whole − part = part.

$10 = 7 + 3$

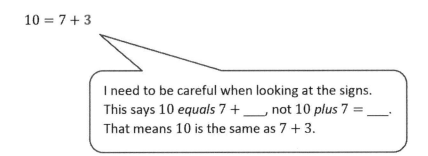

I need to be careful when looking at the signs.
This says 10 *equals* 7 + ___, not 10 *plus* 7 = ___.
That means 10 is the same as $7 + 3$.

G2-M1-Lesson 2

Fluency Practice

Making the next ten and adding to a multiple of ten is foundational to future Grade 2 strategies. Students continue to use a number bond to show the part-whole relationship with numbers.

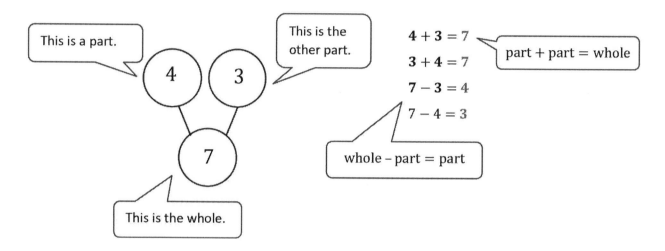

1. $30 + 6 = 36$

   I can add 3 tens and 6 ones to get 36.

2. $64 = 60 + 4$

   I can break apart 64 into tens and ones.
   64 is 6 tens and 4 ones, so $64 = 60 + 4$.

3. $35 = 30 + 5$

   I can think 35 is 5 and what?

G2-M1-Lesson 3

Add and Subtract Like Units, Ones, To Solve Problems Within 100

1. $20 + 7 = 27$

> $20 + 7 = \underline{\hspace{1cm}}$
> I can think 2 tens + 7 ones = 2 tens 7 ones.
> To solve $20 + 70$ add tens to tens. The units are the same, so I can add them together.
> 2 tens + 7 tens = 9 tens.

2. $20 + 70 = 90$

3. $62 + 3 = 65$

> To solve $62 + 3$ add ones to ones.
> 6 tens 2 ones + 3 ones = 6 tens 5 ones
> To solve $62 + 30$ add tens to tens.
> 6 tens 2 ones + 3 tens = 9 tens 2 ones

4. $62 + 30 = 92$

5. Complete each blank in the table below.

> I can use a related fact to help me solve. I know $4 + 5 = 9$, so $24 + 5 = 29$.

> I can think 2 tens + 5 tens = 7 tens. I can break apart 24 and draw a number bond if I need help seeing the units.

> I can draw tens and ones to help me. Now it is easy to see 8 ones - 3 ones is 5 ones, and the 7 tens did not change.

a. $24 + 5 = \underline{29}$	b. $24 + 50 = \underline{74}$ 20 4
c. $78 - 3 = \underline{75}$ 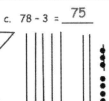	d. $78 - 30 = \underline{48}$

G2-M1-Lesson 4

Making Ten from an Addend of 9, 8, or 7

1. $9 + 3 = 12$

X
O
O
O
O

O O O O O

O X
O X

> I can draw 9 circles and 3 Xs to add.
>
> I see that I made a ten! Now it is easy to add because I know $10 + 2$ is 12.

2. $8 + 7 = 15$

   /\
   2 5

   $8 + 2 = 10$

   $10 + 5 = 15$

> I can also solve without a drawing.
>
> 8 is closer to 10 than 7, so I can make 10 with the 8.
>
> 8 needs 2 to make 10, so I can break apart 7 with a number bond to get the 2 out.
>
> Now I can add 8 and 2 to get 10, and now it is easy to add what is left; 10 and 5 is 15.
>
> So $8 + 7$ is 15.

3. $10 + 2 = 12$

> To solve, I can think 10 and what make 12? 10 and 2 make 12.

4. $9 + 3 = 12$

> I know 9 is 1 less than 10, so the answer for $9 + \_ = 12$ must be 1 more than $10 + \_ = 12$.
>
> So $9 + 3 = 12$.

Lesson 4:   Make a ten to add within 20.

EUREKA
MATH

©2015 Great Minds. eureka-math.org
G2-M1-HWH-1.3.0-07.2015

5. Ronnie uses 5 brown bricks and 8 red bricks to build a fort. How many bricks does Ronnie use in all?

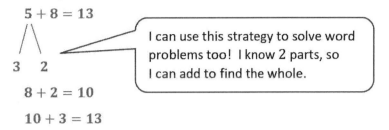

$$5 + 8 = 13$$

3   2

$$8 + 2 = 10$$

$$10 + 3 = 13$$

I can use this strategy to solve word problems too! I know 2 parts, so I can add to find the whole.

Ronnie used 13 bricks in all.

G2-M1-Lesson 5

Making the Next Ten

1. $9 + 3 = 12$

    X
    O
    O
    O
    O

    O
    O
    O
    O X
    O X

    > If I need to, I can draw circles and Xs to add.
    > I see that I made a ten! Now it is easy to add because I know $10 + 2$ is 12.

2. $19 + 3 = 22$
    /\
    1 2

    > I know 19 is really close to a ten, 20. It just needs 1 more.
    > I can break apart 3 with a number bond to get the 1 out.
    > Now I can add 19 and 1 to get 20, and it is easy to add 20 and 2.
    > So, $19 + 3$ is 22.

    $19 + 1 = 20$
    $20 + 2 = 22$

3. $38 + 7 = $ _____
    /\
    2 5

    > 38 is close to 40. I know $8 + 2 = 10$, so 38 needs 2 more to make the next ten.
    >
    > I can break apart the 7 into 2 and 5 to get 2 out.
    >
    > In my head, I can add $38 + 2$ to get 40. Now, I just add what is left, $40 + 5$ is 45, so $38 + 7 = 45$.

4. $8 + 78 = $ _____
    /\
    6 2

    > Using this strategy is easy because I:
    > - Can break apart numbers, like 8 into 6 and 2.
    > - Know 8 ones need 2 ones to make 10, so $78 + 2 = 80$.
    > - Know how to add tens and some ones, like $80 + 6$.

    $78 + 2 = 80$
    $80 + 6 = 86$

Lesson 5:   Make a ten to add within 100.

EUREKA MATH

©2015 Great Minds. eureka-math.org
G2-M1-HWH-1.3.0-07.2015

G2-M1-Lesson 6

1. $20 - 9 = \underline{}11\underline{}$

I can draw 20 and show how I will take 9 from a ten.

Now I see 10 and 1 left, which is 11. So, $20 - 9$ is 11.

2. $30 - 7 = \underline{}23\underline{}$

20 10

$10 - 7 = 3$

$20 + 3 = 23$

I can solve without drawing, too!

First, I break apart 30 with a number bond to take out 10.

Next, I take 7 from 10. I know from my partners to ten that is 3.

$20 + 3 = 23$, so $30 - 7$ is 23.

3. $50 - 8 = \underline{\ 42\ }$

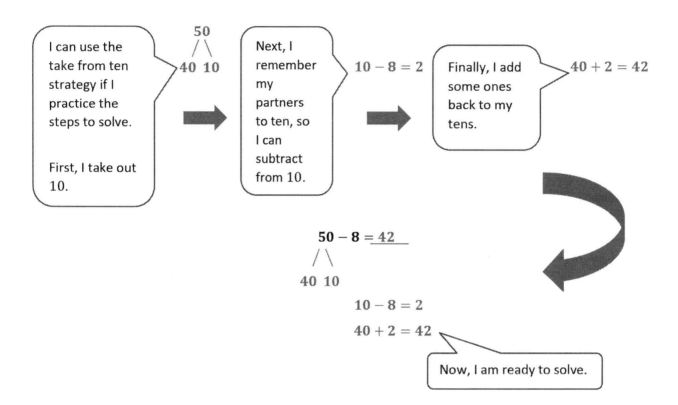

$$\mathbf{50 - 8} = \underline{\ 42\ }$$

$$10 - 8 = 2$$

$$40 + 2 = 42$$

Now, I am ready to solve.

EUREKA MATH

©2015 Great Minds. eureka-math.org
G2-M1-HWH-1.3.0-07.2015

G2-M1-Lesson 7

Take from 10

1. $12 - 9 = 3$

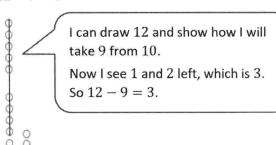

I can draw 12 and show how I will take 9 from 10.

Now I see 1 and 2 left, which is 3. So $12 - 9 = 3$.

$12 - 9 = 3$

2   10

$10 - 9 = 1$
$2 + 1 = 3$

I can solve without drawing too! I can break apart 12 into 2 and 10. Now, it is easy to take 9 from 10. $10 - 9$ is 1. And then I just add what is left. $2 + 1$ is 3.

So, $12 - 9$ is 3.

2. $14 - 8 = 6$

First, take out 10.

$14 - 8 = \underline{}$

4   10

Now, subtract from 10.

$10 - 8 = 2$

And adding what is left is easy because I know my related facts.

$2 + 4 = 6$

So $14 - 8 = 6.$

3. Shane has 12 pencils. He gives some pencils to his friends. Now, he has 7 left. How many pencils did he give away?

$12 - 7 = 5$

2   10

$10 - 7 = 3$
$3 + 2 = 5$

Shane gave away 5 pencils.

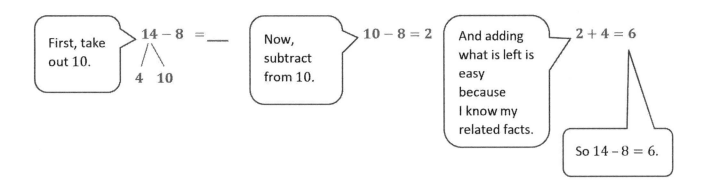

I can use this strategy to solve word problems, too!

I know the whole and a part. That means a part is missing! I can subtract to find how many pencils Shane gave away.

G2-M1-Lesson 8

Take from 10

> I can use the same take from ten strategy when subtracting from bigger numbers!

> I can break apart 52 into 42 and 10. Now it is easy to take away 9. I know from the partners to ten that $10 - 9$ is 1. Now I just add what is left. $42 + 1$ is 43.

1. $12 - 9 = 3$

    $\diagup \diagdown$

    $2 \quad 10$

    $\qquad 10 - 9 = 1$

    $\qquad 2 + 1 = 3$

    $\Longrightarrow$

    $52 - 9 = 43$

    $\diagup \diagdown$

    $42 \quad 10$

    $\qquad 10 - 9 = 1$

    $\qquad 42 + 1 = 43$

2. $61 - 5 = \underline{\quad 56 \quad}$

> Let's get ready to use this strategy! Let's take out 10.

$61 - 5$

$\diagup \diagdown$

$51 \quad 10$

> Now, let's practice subtracting from 10.

$10 - 5 = 5$

> And adding what is left is easy because I know my related facts.

$51 + 5 = 56$

3. Mrs. Watts had 12 tacos. The children ate some. Nine tacos were left. How many tacos did the children eat?

    $12 - 9 = \underline{\quad}$

    $\diagup \diagdown$

    $2 \quad 10$

    $\qquad 10 - 9 = 1$

    $\qquad 2 + 1 = 3$

    The children ate 3 tacos.

> I can use this strategy to solve word problems, too!
>
> I know the whole and a part. That means a part is missing! I can subtract to find how many tacos the children ate.

Lesson 8:   Take from 10 within 100.

EUREKA MATH

Homework Helpers

Grade 2
Module 2

G2-M2-Lesson 1

1. The length of the picture of the shovel is about __8__ centimeters.

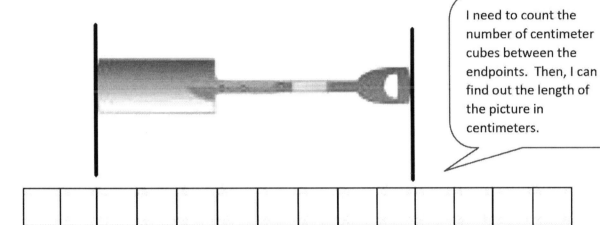

> I need to count the number of centimeter cubes between the endpoints. Then, I can find out the length of the picture in centimeters.

2. The length of a screwdriver is 19 centimeters. The handle is 5 centimeters long. What is the length of the top of the screwdriver?

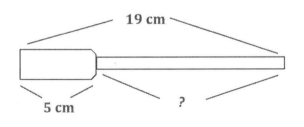

19 cm

5 cm   ?

$5 + \underline{\ \ } = 19$

The top of the screwdriver is 14 centimeters.

> I can use the Read-Draw-Write process to solve. I can draw a screwdriver and label the whole length 19 cm. This is just like lining up my centimeter cubes! I know one part is 5 centimeters, so I'll label that. I can use addition to solve for the unknown part, which is 14 cm. I can write a complete statement of my answer.

G2-M2-Lesson 2

1. The picture of the eraser is about ___4___ centimeters long.

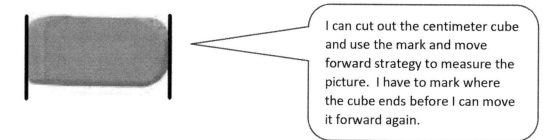

> I can cut out the centimeter cube and use the mark and move forward strategy to measure the picture. I have to mark where the cube ends before I can move it forward again.

2. John used a centimeter cube and the mark and move forward strategy to measure these pieces of tape. Use his work to answer the following questions.

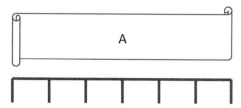   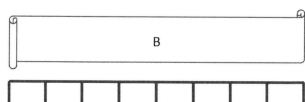

How long is Tape A? ___6___ centimeters long.   How long is Tape B? ___8___ centimeters long.

Which tape is shorter? _____Tape A_____

The total length of Tapes A and B is __14__ centimeters.

> Since John measured without any gaps or overlaps, I know that the distance between the pencil marks is the same length! I can count the length units for each piece of tape.

2   Lesson 2:   Use iteration with one physical unit to measure.

EUREKA MATH

G2-M2-Lesson 3

Use your centimeter ruler to answer the following questions.

1. The picture of the animal track is about ___4___ cm long.

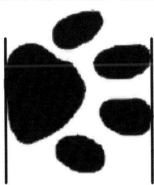

I know how to accurately line up my centimeter ruler to measure the picture of the animal track. Since my hash marks are labeled, I don't have to count each mark; I can easily see that the picture is 4 centimeters long.

2. Measure the lengths of sides A, B, and C. Write each length on the line.

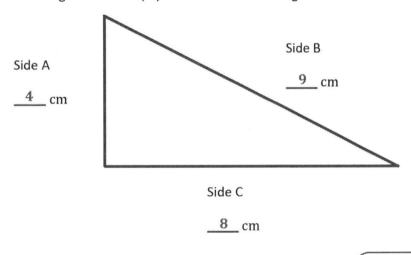

Side A

___4___ cm

Side B

___9___ cm

Side C

___8___ cm

How much shorter is Side C than Side B? ___1___ cm

$$9 - 8 = 1$$

I can use my centimeter ruler to measure the length of each side. Then, I can compare the lengths of two sides by subtracting.

G2-M2-Lesson 4

1. Circle cm (centimeter) or m (meter) to show which unit you would use to measure the length of each object.

Length of a glue stick   (cm)   or   m

Length of a door   cm   or   (m)

Length of the teacher's desk   cm   or   (m)

Length of a marker   (cm)   or   m

> I know that the door and teacher's desk are longer than 100 centimeters, so I can measure with my meter stick.

2. Fill in the blanks with cm or m.

The height of the building is 12 __m__ .

The length of the blue thread was 8 __cm__ longer than the red thread.

The runner broke the record for the 500 __m__ dash.

> I can use my number sense here. I don't think a runner would break a record for a 500 centimeter dash; that's only 5 meter sticks long! The answer must be in meters.

3. Use the centimeter ruler below to find the length (from one mark to the next) of the shape.

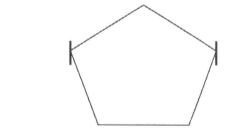

The shape is __4__ cm long.

> The endpoints of the shape line up to the 2 cm and 6 cm mark on the ruler. I can begin at 2 centimeters and count up 4 centimeters until I get to 6 centimeters.

1 2 3 4 5 6 7 8 9 10

Lesson 4:   Measure various objects using centimeter rulers and meter sticks.

EUREKA MATH

G2-M2-Lesson 5

1. Name two things in school that you would measure in meters. Estimate their lengths.

Item	Estimated Length
chalkboard	*4 meters*
reading corner rug	*3 meters*

> I know that the length from the doorknob to the floor is about 1 meter. So I think the reading corner rug is about 3 of those lengths. The rug looks shorter than the chalkboard, so I can estimate that the rug is about 3 meters long.

2. Choose the best length estimate for each object.

   a. Bulletin board   (2 m) or   35 cm

   b. Scissors   (13 cm) or   43 cm

   c. Top of a student desk   18 cm or   (62 cm)

> I know that a 3-ring binder is about 30 centimeters long. I can picture 2 of those binders fitting across the length of my desktop, which would be about 60 centimeters long.
> So, 62 centimeters is closer to 60 centimeters than 18 centimeters.

3. Measure the length of the line below using your pinky finger. Write your estimate.

   Estimate: ___7___ cm

> Since the width of my pinky finger is about 1 centimeter, I can estimate that the length of the line is about 7 centimeters.

EUREKA MATH   Lesson 5:   Develop estimation strategies by applying prior knowledge of length and using mental benchmarks.   5

©2015 Great Minds. eureka-math.org
G2-M1-HWH-1.3.0-07.2015

G2-M2-Lesson 6

1. Measure each set of lines in centimeters, and write the length on the line. Complete the comparison sentences.

Line A
_____

Line B _____

Line C _____

> I can lay my meter strip along each line to measure its length. I need to line up the zero point on my ruler with the endpoint of the line!

Line A	Line B	Line C
__15__ cm	__5__ cm	__8__ cm

Lines A, B, and C are about ___28___ cm combined.

Line C is about ___7___ cm shorter than Line A.

> Since Line A is 15 cm long and Line C is 8 cm long, I know that Line C is shorter. I can subtract: $15 - 8 = 7$. Line C is 7 cm shorter than Line A.

2. Line D is 45 cm long. Line E is 70 cm long. Line F is 1 m long.

Line E is ___25___ cm longer than Line D.

Line E doubled is ___40___ cm longer than Line F.

> I know that 1 meter equals 100 centimeters. If I double Line E, then it will be 140 cm long because $70 + 70 = 140$. 140 centimeters is 40 centimeters more than 100 centimeters.

3. Lanie measured the height of her little brother. He is 52 cm tall.

How much taller is a meter stick than her brother? ___48___ cm.

$$52 + \underline{} = 100$$
$$52 + 8 = 60$$
$$60 + 40 = 100$$
$$8 + 40 = 48$$

> This is like a missing addend problem. I can solve by adding on. I want to get to 100 because a meter stick is 100 cm long. I know that $52 + 8$ will get me to the friendly number 60. Then, $60 + 40 = 100$. And, $8 + 40 = 48$.

Lesson 6: Measure and compare lengths using centimeters and meters.

EUREKA MATH™

©2015 Great Minds. eureka-math.org
G2-M1-HWH-1.3.0-07.2015

G2-M2-Lesson 7

1. Measure each line with one small paper clip, using the mark and move forward method. Then, measure in centimeters using a ruler.

_____ Line A

_____ Line B

Line A	__3__ paper clips	__9__ cm
Line B	__1__ paper clips	__3__ cm

Line A is about __2__ paper clips longer than Line B.

Line B doubled is about __3__ cm shorter than Line A because I know $6 + 3 = 9$.

> I know that Line B is 3 cm long. If I double its length, then it will be 6 cm long. I can use mental math to figure out that Line B doubled is 3 cm shorter than Line A because I know $6 + 3 = 9$.

2. Christina measured Line C with quarters and pennies.

Line C

Why did Christina need more pennies than quarters to measure Line C?

Since the quarter is bigger, it takes fewer quarters to measure the same line. If the length unit

is smaller, like a penny, then you need a greater number of pennies to measure the line.

> If the unit size is bigger, like quarters, then you need fewer units. If the unit size is smaller, like pennies, then you need more units. Coins aren't a good measurement tool. Centimeters are much more reliable because each length unit is the same!

EUREKA MATH   Lesson 7:   Measure and compare lengths using standard metric length units and non-standard length units; relate measurement to unit size.   7

©2015 Great Minds. eureka-math.org
G2-M1-HWH-1.3.0-07.2015

G2-M2-Lesson 8

1.

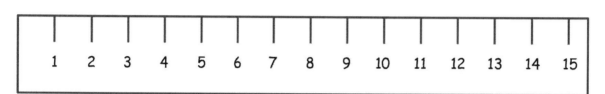

A _____

B _____

| 1 | 2 | 3 | 4 | 5 | 6 | 7 | 8 | 9 | 10 | 11 | 12 | 13 | 14 | 15 |

Line A is __8__ cm. $14 - 6 = 8$ Line B is __9__ cm. $11 - 2 = 9$

Lines A and B are __17__ cm. $8 + 9 = 17$

Line A is __1__ cm (longer(shorter)) than Line B.

> Since Line B starts at 2 cm, I can take away 2 cm from where the line ends at 11 cm. So, the line is 9 cm.

2. A cricket jumped 5 centimeters forward and 9 centimeters back and then stopped. If the cricket started at 23 on the ruler, where did the cricket stop? Show your work on the broken centimeter ruler.

$23 + 5 = 28$ $28 - 9 = 18 + 1 = 19$
                              /\
                            18 10

> I can use addition and subtraction to solve. I can start at 23 and count on 5. Then, I can hop back 9 centimeters or subtract 9. The cricket stops at 19 cm.

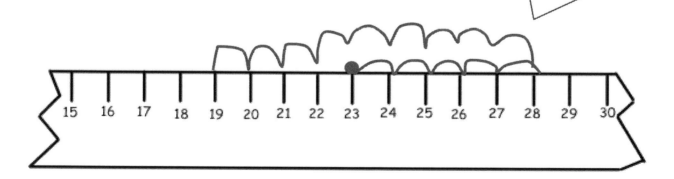

| 15 | 16 | 17 | 18 | 19 | 20 | 21 | 22 | 23 | 24 | 25 | 26 | 27 | 28 | 29 | 30 |

Lesson 8:   Solve addition and subtraction word problems using the ruler as a number line.

EUREKA MATH™

3. All of the parts of the path below are equal length units. Fill in the lengths of each side.

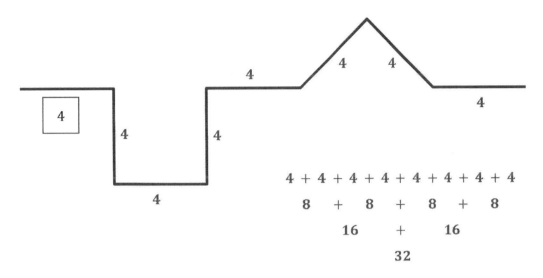

The path is __32__ length units long.

How many more parts would you need to add for the path to be 40 length units long?   __2__ parts

> I know that the path is 32 length units. I can think
> 32 + __ = 40. The unknown is 8 length units.
> But the question asks for the number of parts.
> I know that each part is 4 length units. So, 2 more
> parts, 4 + 4, equals 8.

G2-M2-Lesson 9

1. Tommy completed the chart below by first estimating the measurement around three body parts and then finding the actual measurement with his meter strip.

Body Part Measured	Estimated Measurement in Centimeters	Actual Measurement in Centimeters
Neck	25 cm	31 cm
Wrist	13 cm	17 cm
Head	50 cm	57 cm

What is the difference between the longest and shortest measurements?

__40__ cm $57 - 17 = 40$

Draw a tape diagram comparing the measurements of Tommy's neck and wrist.

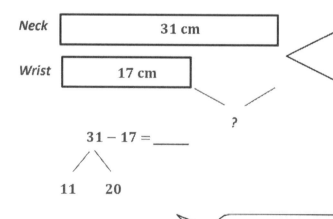

Neck   31 cm

Wrist   17 cm

?

$31 - 17 = $ ____

11   20

$20 - 17 = 3$

$11 + 3 = 14$

I can draw a tape diagram to compare measurements. The longer bar represents the length around Tommy's neck. The shorter bar represents the length around his wrist. I must remember to draw the second bar directly underneath the first. I have to make sure that they line up perfectly so that the starting points are at the same place.

I can describe the difference by writing the expression $31 - 17$. Then, I can draw a number bond and use the take from ten strategy to solve.

Lesson 9:   Measure lengths of string using measurement tools, and use tape diagrams to represent and compare lengths.

©2015 Great Minds. eureka-math.org
G2-M1-HWH-1.3.0-07.2015

EUREKA MATH

2. Measure the two paths below with your meter strip and string.

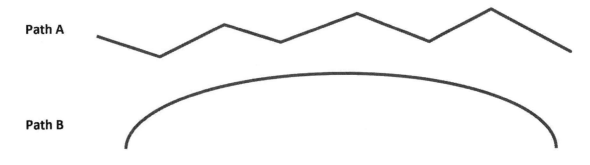

Path A

Path B

Path A is ____14____ cm long.

Path B is ____13____ cm long.

I can lay my string straight along each path. Then, I can lay it along the meter strip to figure out the actual length in centimeters.

Together, Paths A and B measure ____27____ cm. $14 + 13 = 27$

Path A is ____1____ cm (shorter/longer) than Path B. $14 - 13 = 1$

EUREKA
MATH™

Lesson 9:   Measure lengths of string using measurement tools, and use tape diagrams to represent and compare lengths.

11

©2015 Great Minds. eureka-math.org
G2-M1-HWH-1.3.0-07.2015

G2-M2-Lesson 10

Use the Read-Draw-Write (RDW) process to solve. Draw a tape diagram for each step.

Jesse's tower of blocks is 30 cm tall. Sarah's tower is 9 cm shorter than Jesse's tower. What is the total height of both towers?

Step 1: Find the height of Sarah's tower.

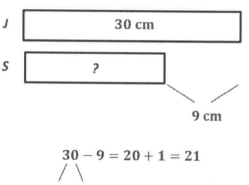

I can draw a tape diagram to compare Jesse and Sarah's towers. I don't know how tall Sarah's tower is, so I can label it with a question mark. But, I know that Sarah's tower is shorter, so I can draw arms and label the difference with 9 cm. I can use subtraction and the take from ten strategy to find the missing part, so $30 - 9 = 21$.

$$30 - 9 = 20 + 1 = 21$$

$$20 \quad 10$$

$$10 - 9 = 1$$

$$20 + 1 = 21$$ *Sarah's tower is 21 cm.*

Step 2: Find the total height of both towers.

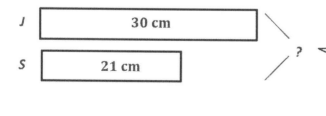

From Step 1, I know that Sarah's tower is 21 cm. Now, I can label Sarah's bar with 21 cm. I can add both parts together to find the whole. 30 cm + 21 cm = 51 cm.

$$30 + 21 = ?$$

$$30 + 21 = 51$$

The total height of both towers is 51 cm.

Lesson 10:   Apply conceptual understanding of measurement by solving two-step word problems.

©2015 Great Minds. eureka-math.org
G2-M1-HWH-1.3.0-07.2015

EUREKA
MATH™

Homework Helpers

Grade 2
Module 3

G2-M3-Lesson 1

1. Fill in the missing part.

   a.   3 ones + __7__ ones = 10 ones

   b.   3 + __7__ = 10

   c.   3 tens + __7__ tens = 1 hundred

   d.   30 + __70__ = 100

   > I know 3 facts that can help me solve all these problems:
   > $3 + 7 = 10$
   > 10 ones = 1 ten
   > 10 tens = 1 hundred

2. Rewrite in order from largest to smallest units.

4 tens	Largest	_2 hundreds_
2 hundreds		_4 tens_
9 ones	Smallest	_9 ones_

   > I know that 2 hundreds equal 200, 4 tens equal 40, and 9 ones equal 9.

3. Count each group. What is the total number of sticks in each group?

Bundles of 100	Bundles of 10	Ones
200	30	6

   What is the total number of sticks? __236__

4. Draw and solve.

Moses has 100 stickers. Jared has 80 stickers. Jared wants to have the same number of stickers as Moses. How many more stickers does Jared need?

I can start at 80 and count on by 10's until I reach 100.

Jared needs __20__ more stickers

I can draw bundles of 10 to help me keep count: 90, 100.

I counted 2 more tens. That's 20.

Lesson 1:   Bundle and count ones, tens, and hundreds to 1,000.

EUREKA MATH

G2-M3-Lesson 2

1. These are bundles with 10 sticks in each.

   a. How many tens are there? __11__

   b. How many hundreds? __1__

   c. How many sticks in all? __110__

   > I count 11 tens. I know that 10 tens equal 1 hundred. I can skip-count by tens to see that there are 110 sticks in all.

2. Dean did some counting. Look at his work. Explain why you think Dean counted this way.

   $$128, 129, 130, 140, 150, 160, 170, 180, 181, 182, 183$$

   > Benchmark numbers allow us to skip-count, which is faster than counting by ones. So Dean counted by ones to get to the closest benchmark number, 130. Then, he skip-counted by tens up to 180. Next, he counted by ones to reach 183.

3. Show a way to count from 76 to 140 using tens and ones. Explain why you chose to count this way.

   $$76, 77, 78, 79, 80, 90, 100, 110, 120, 130, 140$$

   > I counted by ones to get to the nearest benchmark number after 76, which is 80. Then it was easy to skip-count by tens up to 140.

©2015 Great Minds. eureka-math.org
G2-M1-HWH-1.3.0-07.2015

G2-M3-Lesson 3

> I count by ones to reach 70. I count by tens to reach 100. I count by hundreds to reach 400, and then I count by tens to get to 420.

1. Fill in the blanks to reach the benchmark numbers.

66, __67__, __68__, __69__, 70, __80__, __90__, 100, __200__, __300__, 400, __410__, 420

> Benchmark numbers make it quicker and easier to count to large numbers!

2. These are ones, tens, and hundreds. How many sticks are there in all?

> I know that the order of these drawn units doesn't matter, but it's easiest to start with the highest value, the hundreds.

> This shows 2 hundreds, 3 tens, and 2 ones. I can count like this: 100, 200, 210, 220, 230, 231, 232. So there are 232 sticks in all.

There are __232__ sticks in all.

3. Show a way to count from 457 to 700 using ones, tens, and hundreds.

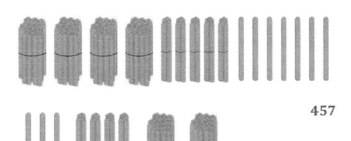

457

> I count three more ones to get to the benchmark number, 460. From there I can count by tens up to 500. Then, I count on by hundreds to reach 700.

> I can draw bundles to show my count or just write the numbers.

458, 459, 460, 470, 480, 490, 500, 600, 700

EUREKA MATH

G2-M3-Lesson 4

1. Pilar used the place value chart to count bundles. How many sticks does she have in all?

Hundreds	Tens	Ones

Pilar has __135__ sticks.

> I see 1 hundred, 3 tens, and 5 ones. I count the units like this, 100, 110, 120, 130, 131, 132, 133, 134, 135. I can also count in unit form like this, 1 hundred 3 tens 5 ones.

2. These are tens. If you put them together, which unit will you make?

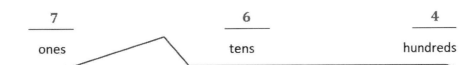

> I can skip-count by ten to see that 10 tens equal 1 hundred.
> 10, 20, 30, 40, 50, 60, 70, 80, 90, 100.
> I can bundle it to show 100.

    a. one   b. hundred   c. thousand   d. ten

3. Imagine 467 on the place value chart. How many ones, tens, and hundreds are in each place?

    7   6   4
   ones   tens   hundreds

> I have to pay attention to the order of the units! On the place value chart, the order would be 4 hundreds first, then 6 tens, and then 7 ones.

4. Show a way to count from 160 to 530 using tens and hundreds. Circle at least one benchmark number.

    160, 170, 180, 190, 200, 300, 400, 500, 510, 520, 530

> I skip-count by tens to reach 200. After that, I can count on by hundreds. At 500, I count by tens to reach 530.

G2-M3-Lesson 5

1. What is the value of the 5 in | 8 | 5 | 9 | ?   __50__

    | 800 |
    | 50 |
    | 9 |

    > I can picture how this number looks when shown with Hide Zero cards. The digit 5 is in the tens place. I know the value of 5 tens is 50.

2. Make a number bond to show the hundreds, tens, and ones in the number. Then, write the number in unit form.

    718

    7 hundreds 1 ten 8 ones

    (718)
      / | \
    700 10   8

    > The number bond and unit form both help me see the value of each digit.

3. Draw a line to match unit form with number form.

    a.   4 hundreds 1 ten =   41

    b.   4 tens 1 one =   410

    c.   4 hundreds 1 one = ————— 401

    > I can visualize the numbers on the place value chart to help me match the unit form to number form.

Lesson 5:   Write base ten three-digit numbers in unit form; show the value of each digit.   EUREKA MATH

G2-M3-Lesson 6

1. Match the numerals with the number names.

   a. 216   two hundred sixty

   b. 260   two hundred sixteen

> I have to think about the value of each digit. 216 has 2 hundreds 1 ten 6 ones, and that's two hundred sixteen. 260 has 2 hundreds 6 tens, and that's two hundred sixty.

2. Write the answer in number form.

   a. $1 + 1 + 1 + 10 + 10 + 100 + 100 + 100 + 100 =$ __423__

   b. __187__ $= 7 + 100 + 80$

   c. __320__ $= 300 + 20$

> This addition problem tells the total value of each unit. The expanded form is not in order. I have to be careful when writing the number to put it in order from largest to smallest unit.

> When I add the total value of each unit, I get $3 + 20 + 400$. That's the same as $400 + 20 + 3$ because I know I can write the units in any order, and the total stays the same. So, the answer is 423.

3. Write each number in expanded form.

   a. $26 =$ __$20 + 6$__

   b. $720 =$ __$700 + 20$__

   c. $403 =$ __$400 + 3$__

> Writing the numbers as addition sentences with the parts representing the total value of each unit helps me see the value of each place.

> When there is a zero for one of the units, I do not write the 0 in the expanded form.

G2-M3-Lesson 7

1. These are bundles of hundreds, tens, and ones. Write the standard form, expanded form, and word form for each number shown.

> The order of the units doesn't change the total, so the number in standard form is 513.

   a.   Standard Form   513

   b.   Expanded Form $500 + 10 + 3$

   c.   Word Form   *Five hundred thirteen*

> The digit 6 is in the tens place. I know the value of 6 tens is 60.

2. What is the unit value of the 6 in 261?   60

> All the numbers use the digits 1 and 4 but in different places. Using what I know about place value helps me solve.

3. Write 141, 114, 411, in order from greatest to least.

   411   141   114

> Hundreds are the biggest unit, so a number with 4 hundreds is bigger than a number with 1 hundred.

> 141 comes next because it has more tens in the tens place than 114.

> I can also think of it like this: 141 has 14 tens, but 114 has only 11 tens.

©2015 Great Minds. eureka-math.org
G2-M1-HWH-1.3.0-07.2015

G2-M3-Lesson 8

> Counting to find the value of $1, $10, and $100 bills is just like counting ones, tens, and hundreds!

1. Write the total value of the money.

$100	$100	$10	$1	$1
$100	$10	$10	$1	$1

$334

> I count, starting with the largest unit, $100, 200, 300, 310, 320, 330, 331, 332, 333, 334.$

> I can use what I know about expanded form to work with money. $\$400 + \$10 + \$5 = \$415.$

2. Fill in the bills with $100, $10, or $1 to show the amount.

$100	$100	$100	$100	$10
$1	$1	$1	$1	$1

$415

3. Draw and solve.

Jill has 5 ten-dollar bills and 3 one-dollar bills. Ben has 2 fewer ten-dollar bills and 1 fewer one-dollar bill than Jill. What is the value of Ben's money?

$~~10~~	$~~10~~	$10	$10	$10
$~~1~~	$1	$1		

Ben has $32.

> I can draw Jill's bills and then cross off to show Ben's money. Then, I count what is left, 10, 20, 30, 31, 32. Ben has $32.

©2015 Great Minds. eureka-math.org
G2-M1-HWH-1.3.0-07.2015

G2-M3-Lesson 9

1. Show one way to count from $67 to $317.

    $67, 77, 87, 97, 107, 117, 217, 317$

    > Counting money is just like counting with numerals, so I can leave off the dollar signs and just skip-count by tens to get to 117. Then, I skip-count by hundreds to get to 317.

2. Use each number line to show a different way to count from $280 to $523.

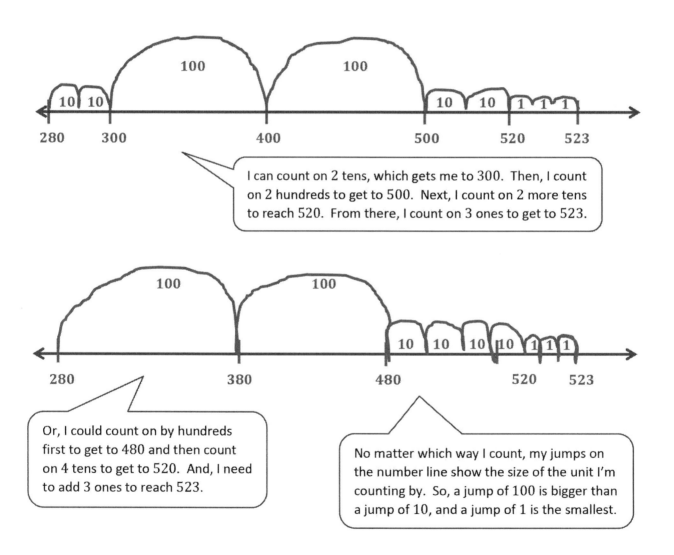

> I can count on 2 tens, which gets me to 300. Then, I count on 2 hundreds to get to 500. Next, I count on 2 more tens to reach 520. From there, I count on 3 ones to get to 523.

> Or, I could count on by hundreds first to get to 480 and then count on 4 tens to get to 520. And, I need to add 3 ones to reach 523.

> No matter which way I count, my jumps on the number line show the size of the unit I'm counting by. So, a jump of 100 is bigger than a jump of 10, and a jump of 1 is the smallest.

©2015 Great Minds. eureka-math.org
G2-M1-HWH-1.3.0-07.2015

G2-M3-Lesson 10

I skip-count by hundreds up to 500 because I know 10 tens are in 1 hundred.

How many $10 bills are equal to $500?

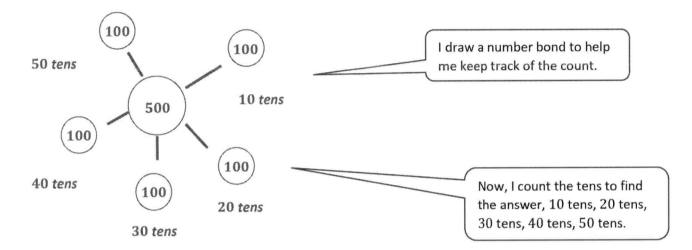

I draw a number bond to help me keep track of the count.

Now, I count the tens to find the answer, 10 tens, 20 tens, 30 tens, 40 tens, 50 tens.

50 *ten-dollar bills are equal to* $500.

Or, I can draw a number line and skip-count by hundreds up to 500. I write 10 tens inside each hop, and then I count how many tens there are in all.

There are 10, 20, 30, 40, 50 tens in all.

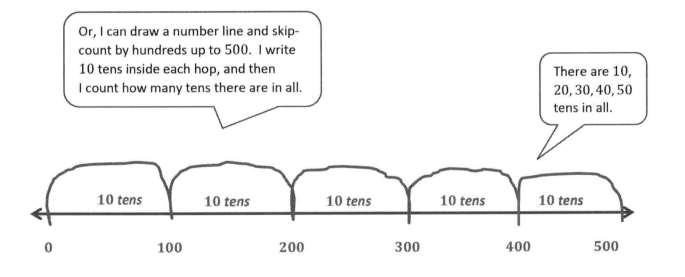

G2-M3-Lesson 11

Students use place value disks to model the value of each digit in a given number. A template has been provided to help students complete the homework assignment.

Model the following numbers for your parent using the fewest disks possible. Whisper the numbers in standard form and unit form.

a. 12

> I could show 12 ones disks, but to use the fewest disks, I show 1 ten and 2 ones.

> In standard form, I say 12. In unit form, I say 1 ten 2 ones.

b. 123
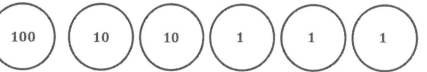

> In standard form, I say 123. In unit form, I say 1 hundred 2 tens 3 ones.

> I could show 12 tens disks and 3 ones disks, but to use the fewest disks, I show 1 hundred, 2 tens, and 3 ones.

c. 103

> In standard form, I say 103. In unit form, I say 1 hundred 3 ones.

> In standard form, I say 330. In unit form, I say 3 hundreds 3 tens.

d. 330

©2015 Great Minds. eureka-math.org
G2-M1-HWH-1.3.0-07.2015

G2-M3-Lesson 12

Students complete this chart as they work with place value disks.

Count from 582 to 700 using place value disks. Change for a larger unit when necessary.

When you counted from 582 to 700:

Did you make a larger unit at...	Yes, I changed to make:		No, I need _____
1. 590?	(1 ten)	1 hundred	___ ones. ___ tens.
2. 600?	1 ten	(1 hundred)	___ ones. ___ tens.
3. 618?	1 ten	1 hundred	_2_ ones. ___ tens.
4. 640?	(1 ten)	1 hundred	___ ones. ___ tens.
5. 652?	1 ten	1 hundred	_8_ ones. ___ tens.
6. 700?	1 ten	(1 hundred)	___ ones. ___ tens.

When I add 8 ones to 582, I make the next ten. Now I'm at 590.

Counting on from 590, when I add 10 more ones, I make a ten, which also means I make a new hundred, 600.

I need to add 2 more ones to make a new ten and reach 620.

I make a new ten when I reach 630, and again when I reach 640.

I need to add 8 more ones to make a new ten and reach 660.

Counting on from 690, when I add 10 more ones, I make a ten, which also means I make a new hundred, 700.

G2-M3-Lesson 13

Draw place value disks to show the numbers.

> Drawing place value disks helps me see the value of each digit. I can see that the digit 7 equals 70, and the digit 2 is just 2 ones.

a.   72

(10) (10) (10) (10) (10) (10) (10)   (1) (1)

> I draw the disks like a ten-frame, starting from the top down in each place. I fill a column of 5 and then start from the bottom up to build toward the other five for 6, 7, 8, or 9. This makes it easy to see when I make a new unit.

> It's easy to see that if I add 8 more ones, I'll make a new unit of ten. If I add 3 more tens, I'll make a new unit of 1 hundred.

b.   303

(100) (100) (100)   (1) (1) (1)

> When I say the number in unit form, 3 hundreds 3 ones, and I draw place value disks, I understand the value of each 3.

©2015 Great Minds. eureka-math.org
G2-M1-HWH-1.3.0-07.2015

G2-M3-Lesson 14

1. Whisper-talk the numbers and words as you fill in the blanks.

> I know 18 is 1 ten 8 ones. I can exchange 1 ten for 10 ones and have 10 ones and 8 ones, which is 18 ones.

a. 18 = _____ hundreds __1__ tens __8__ ones

18 = __18__ ones

> I can say 315 is 3 hundreds 1 ten 5 ones. Since I know 1 ten 5 ones is the same as 15 ones, I can also say 315 is 3 hundreds 15 ones.

b. 315 = __3__ hundreds __1__ tens __5__ ones

315 = __3__ hundreds __15__ ones

c. 419 = __4__ hundreds __1__ tens __9__ ones

419 = __41__ tens __9__ ones

> I know 10 tens make 100, so there are 40 tens in 400. Then, I add the other ten, so there are 41 tens. The ones stay the same.

d. 570 = __5__ hundreds __7__ tens

570 = __57__ tens

> Problem (c) helps me solve this one. I know 40 tens are in 400, so 50 tens are in 500. 50 tens plus 7 tens equals 57 tens!

2. Write down how you can skip-count by ten from 420 to 310. You might use place value disks, number lines, bundles, or numbers.

$$420, 410, 400, 390, 380, 370, 360, 350, 340, 330, 320, 310$$

> Easy! I can just count back by ten!

G2-M3-Lesson 15

Students follow the steps of the Read, Draw, Write (RDW) process to solve word problems: Read the problem; draw and label a model of the information given; write an equation to solve; write a statement of the answer to the question.

Pencils come in boxes of 10.

a. How many boxes should Kadyn buy if he needs 136 pencils?

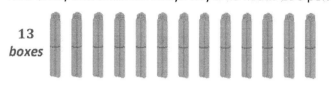

13 boxes

1 box

> Since there are 10 pencils in each box, I can skip-count by ten. I can draw bundles of ten to represent the boxes as I count to 130.

$13 + 1 = 14$

Kadyn should buy 14 boxes.

> I need to draw another box because Kadyn needs 6 more than 130.

> Or, I could use what I've learned about unit form. There are 13 tens 6 ones in 136, so I need 13 boxes to have 130 pencils, plus 1 more box for the extra 6 pencils.

b. How many pencils will Kadyn have left over after he gets what he needs out of the boxes?

$10 - 6 = 4$

Kadyn will have 4 pencils left over.

> Kadyn will use all 130 pencils from the first 13 boxes. Then, he'll need to take 6 pencils out of the last box of ten. That means 4 pencils will be left over.

c. How many more pencils does he need to have 200?

140, 150, 160, 70, 180, 190, 200

I have to be careful and pay attention to what the question is asking. In the first part of this problem, I was solving for *boxes*. This time, the unit I'm solving for is *pencils*! I can skip-count by ten from 140 to 200. So, 150, 160, 170, 180, 190, 200. That is 6 tens, or 60.

Kadyn needs 60 more pencils.

G2-M3-Lesson 16

> Drawing the numbers with disks on the place value chart makes it easy to compare them.

1. Draw the following numbers using place value disks on the place value charts. Answer the questions below.

a. 132   b. 312   c. 213

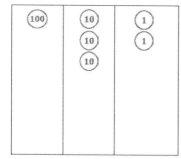   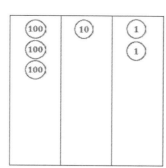   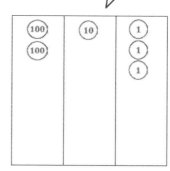

d. Order the numbers from least to greatest: __132__ , __213__ , __312__

> Hundreds are the biggest unit here, and 312 has more hundreds than the other numbers. 132 is the smallest number because it only has 1 hundred.

> You could also compare all the tens in each number. 132 has 13 tens, 213 has 21 tens, and 312 has 31 tens.

2. Circle *less than* or *greater than*. Whisper the complete sentence.

> $300 + 60 + 5 = 365$. 365 is less than 635 because it only has 3 hundreds. 635 has 6 hundreds. I could also think of it as 36 tens is less than 63 tens.

a. $300 + 60 + 5$ is (less than)/ greater than 635.

b. 4 tens and 2 ones is less than /(greater than) 24.

> In this problem, tens are the greatest unit. 4 tens and 2 ones equals 42. 42 is greater than 24 because it has 4 tens, and 24 only has 2 tens. I could also think of it as 40 is greater than 20.

EUREKA MATH

3. Write >, <, or =. Whisper the complete number sentences as you work.

a. 419 (<) 491

> Place value helps me compare the numbers, especially when the digits are all the same. Both numbers have 4 hundreds, so I'm careful to notice which digit is in the tens place. 1 ten is less than 9 tens, so 419 is less than 491.

b. 908 (<) nine hundred eighty

980

> When the problems are written in word form or unit form, I just rewrite them in standard form. Then, it's easy to see the digits in their places. 908 is less than 980. The hundreds are the same, but 0 tens is less than 8 tens.

c. 4 tens 2 ones (=) 30 + 12

42

> 4 tens 2 ones equals 42, and 30 + 12 = 42. That's easy! 42 equals 42.

d. 36 − 10 (>) 2 tens 5 ones

25

> 36 − 10 = 26. 2 tens 5 ones equals 25. 26 is greater than 25.

G2-M3-Lesson 17

> I have to read carefully! In Part (a), the ones are first, and the tens come after, but when placed on the place value chart, the hundreds come first.

> When I whisper count as I draw, I see that I am comparing 112 and 115. 112 is less than 115.

1. Whisper count as you show the numbers with place value disks. Circle >, <, or =.

   a. Draw 12 ones and 1 hundred.   b. Draw 11 tens and 5 ones.

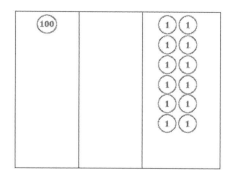
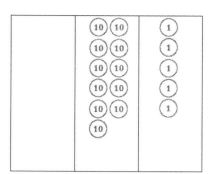

2. Write <, >, or =.

   > I rewrite this problem in standard form, and I'm careful to look at the order of the units. $40 + 9 + 600 = 649$, and 9 ones 64 tens = 649. They are equal!

   a. $40 + 9 + 600$ $=$ 9 ones 64 tens

        649   649

   > I already know 52 has to be less because there are no hundreds in 52. 65 tens − 13 tens equals 52 tens, which is 520.

   b.   65 tens − 13 tens $>$ 52

   > I know 27 ones is the same as 2 tens 7 ones, so 3 hundreds 2 tens 7 ones is 327. I know 84 tens is 840. Comparing the hundreds, I know that 327 is less than 840.

   c.   3 hundreds 27 ones $<$ 84 tens

        Lesson 17:   Compare two three-digit numbers using <, >, and = when there are more
                      than 9 ones or 9 tens.

        EUREKA
        MATH™

G2-M3-Lesson 18

> I could draw these numbers in many different ways, but I want to be efficient. Drawing this way also makes it really easy to compare the numbers.

1. Draw the following values on the place value charts as you think best.

   a. 123   b. 321   c. 231

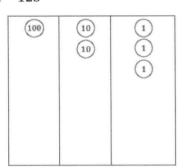 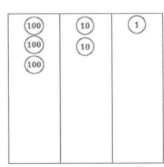 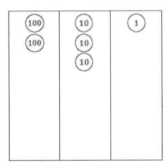

   d. Order the numbers from least to greatest: __123__ , __231__ , __231__

> I can see that 123 has the fewest hundreds, so it is the smallest number. 321 has the most hundreds, so that means it's the biggest number. And 231 is in between.

2. Order the following from least to greatest in standard form.

   three hundred seventy   317   30 tens 7 ones   __307__ , __317__ , __370__

   370   307

> Writing the numbers in standard form helps me see the value. I see that I am comparing 370, 317, and 307.

> Since the hundreds are the same, I compare the tens.

> Careful! This time, the order is from greatest to least.

3. Order the following from greatest to least in standard form.

   4 ones 6 hundreds   46 tens + 10 tens   640   __640__ , __604__ , __560__

   604   56 *tens*

G2-M3-Lesson 19

1. Fill in the chart. Whisper the complete sentence: "____ more/less than ____ is ____."

> I can whisper the complete number sentence as I complete the chart.
> 100 more than 242 is 342.
> 100 less than 242 is 142.
> 10 more than 242 is 252.
> 10 less than 242 is 232.
> 1 more than 242 is 243.
> 1 less than 242 is 241.

	242	153
100 more	342	253
100 less	142	53
10 more	252	163
10 less	232	143
1 more	243	154
1 less	241	152

2. Fill in the blanks. Whisper the complete sentence.

   a. 1 more than 456 is __457__.

   > 1 more than 6 is 7, so 1 more than 456 is 457.

   b. __100__ more than 180 is 280.

   > The hundreds place is now 100 more.

   c. 10 less than __635__ is 625.

   > 10 less than what number is 625? The number I am looking for is 10 more than 625, so it must be 635.

Lesson 19: Model and use language to tell about 1 more and 1 less, 10 more and 10 less, and 100 more and 100 less.

©2015 Great Minds. eureka-math.org
G2-M1-HWH-1.3.0-07.2015

EUREKA MATH™

G2-M3-Lesson 20

1. Fill in the blanks. Whisper the complete sentence.

1 less than 240 is __239__ .

> 1 less than 40 is 39, so 1 less than 240 is 239.
>
> 10 more than 94 is 104, so 10 more than 194 is 204.

10 more than 194 is __204__ .

> I can look to see what changed. 239 changed to 240. 240 is 1 more than 239.
>
> 497 changed to 507. 507 is 10 more than 497.

__1__ more than 239 is 240.

__10__ more than 497 is 507.

10 more than __292__ is 302.

> I can think 10 more than what number is 302? So the number I am looking for is 10 less than 302. That's 292.

2. Whisper the numbers as you count.

> I can count by 1's, 10's. and 100's.

   a. Count by 1's from 396 to 402. $396, 397, 398, 399, 400, 401, 402$

   b. Count by 10's from 396 to 456. $396, 406, 416, 426, 436, 446, 456$

   c. Count by 100's from 396 to 996. $396, 496, 596, 696, 796, 896, 996$

EUREKA MATH™   Lesson 20: Model 1 more and 1 less, 10 more and 10 less, and 100 more and 100 less when changing the hundreds place.   23

©2015 Great Minds. eureka-math.org
G2-M1-HWH-1.3.0-07.2015

G2-M3-Lesson 21

1. Find the pattern. Fill in the blanks.

   a.   497, 498, 499 , 500 , 501

   > 498 is 1 more than 497, so I am counting up by ones. I know 1 more than 99 is 100, so 1 more than 499 is 500.

   b.   571, 581, 591 , 601 , 611

   > 581 is 10 more than 571, so I am counting up by tens. I know 10 more than 90 is 100, so 10 more than 591 is 601.

   c.   133, 123, 113 , 103 , 93

   > 123 is 10 less than 133, so I am counting down by tens. I know 10 less than 100 is 90, so 10 less than 103 is 93.

2. Fill in the chart.

> I can count 1 more or 1 less as I move across the chart. 1 more than 345 is 346. 1 less than 366 is 365. Once I know the pattern, it is easy to complete the chart.

> This puzzle has a pattern! It is like a hundreds chart. I can count 10 more when I move down the chart. 10 more than 348 is 358.

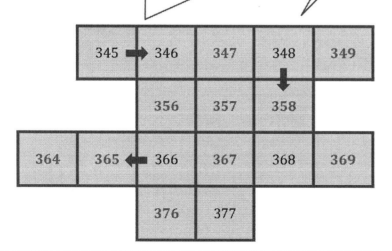

Lesson 21:   Complete a pattern counting up and down.

©2015 Great Minds. eureka-math.org
G2-M1-HWH-1.3.0-07.2015

Grade 2
Module 4

G2-M4-Lesson 1

1. Complete each more or less statement.

   a. 1 less than 46 is 45.

   b. 48 is 10 more than 38.

   c. 63 is 10 less than 73.

   d. 39 is 1 *less than* 40.

   > I can use place value language to explain the change. 1 more and 10 more are the same as adding. 1 less and 10 less are the same as subtracting.

2. Complete each pattern, and write the rule.

   a. 33, 34, 35, 36, 37   Rule: **1** *more*

   b. 43, 33, 23, 13, 3   Rule: **10** *less*

   c. 43, 42, 41, 40, 39   Rule: **1** *less*

   > I study the numbers and look for the more or less pattern. I know 34 is 1 more than 33, so the rule is 1 more.

   > 40 is 1 less than 41, so the rule is 1 less.

3. Label each statement as true or false.

   a. 1 more than 43 is the same as 1 less than 45. *True.*

   b. 10 less than 28 is the same as 1 more than 16. *False.*

   > I know 1 more than 43 is 44, and 1 less than 45 is 44, so this statement is true.
   >
   > 10 less than 28 is 18, and 1 more than 16 is 17, so this statement is false.

4. Below is a chart of fruit in Gloria's basket.

   Use the following to complete the chart.

   - Gloria has 1 more banana than the number of apples.

   - Gloria has 10 fewer oranges than the number of pears.

   > I can use what I know about number patterns to complete the chart. 1 more than 19 is 20, so there are 20 bananas. 10 fewer than 21 is 11, so there are 11 oranges.

Fruit	Number of Fruit
Apples	19
Pears	21
Bananas	20
Oranges	11

G2-M4-Lesson 2

1. Solve using place value strategies. Use the arrow way, number bonds, or mental math, and record your answers.

   a. $48 + 30 = 78$

   / \
   40 8 $40 + 30 = 70$
                 $70 + 8 = 78$

   > To solve $48 + 30$, I think 30 more than 48. I just add like units! $30 + 40 = 70$, and $70 + 8 = 78$. I can draw a number bond to show my thinking.

   b. $27 + 20 = 47$

   $27 \xrightarrow{+20} 47$

   > To solve $27 + \_ = 47$, I count by tens from 27 to 47. I can use the arrow way to show my thinking.

2. Find each sum. Then use $>$, $<$, or $=$ to compare.

   a. $43 + 20 < 30 + 53$

   b. $29 + 50 > 40 + 19$

   > 20 more than 43 is 63, and 30 more than 53 is 83, so 63 is less than 83.

3. Solve using place value strategies.

   a. $35 - 20 = 15$

   b. $46 - 20 = 26$

   > I can draw or solve in my head using place value thinking.
   > 3 tens 5 ones $-$ 2 tens is 1 ten 5 ones, so $35 - 20 = 15$.

4. Complete each more than or less than statement.

   a. 30 less than 78 is **48**.

   b. 45 more than 30 is **75**.

   c. 20 less than **68** is 48.

   d. 40 more than **22** is 62.

   > To solve, I just add like units! 45 more than 30 is the same as $45 + 30$. $40 + 30 = 70$, and $70 + 5 = 75$.

   > 20 less than what number is 48? I can count on to solve! 48, 58, 68. 20 less than 68 is 48.

5. There were 53 papers in the bin after math class. There were 20 papers in the bin before math class. How many papers were added during math class? Use the arrow way to show your simplifying strategy.

   $20 \xrightarrow{+10} 30 \xrightarrow{+10} 40 \xrightarrow{+10} 50 \xrightarrow{+3} 53$

   33 papers were added to the bin during math class.

   > I can start at 20 and count on by tens to 50, and then just add 3 ones to get to 53.

Lesson 2:   Add and subtract multiples of 10 including counting on to subtract.

©2015 Great Minds. eureka-math.org
G2-M1-HWH-1.3.0-07.2015

EUREKA
MATH

G2-M4-Lesson 3

1. Solve using the arrow way.

    a. $48 + 30 = 78$

    > I can use the arrow way to show my thinking. 30 more than 48 is 78. I just add like units, 4 tens plus 3 tens is 7 tens. The 8 ones stay the same.

    $$48 \xrightarrow{+30} 78$$

    $48 + 31 = 79$

    > To add 31, I add 3 tens, and then just add 1 more.

    $$48 \xrightarrow{+30} 78 \xrightarrow{+1} 79$$

    $48 + 29 = 77$

    > Adding 29 is adding 1 less than 30. I add 3 tens, and then just take 1 away.

    $$48 \xrightarrow{+30} 78 \xrightarrow{-1} 77$$

    b. $57 - 40 = 17$

    > 40 less than 57 is 17. I just subtract like units. 5 tens minus 4 tens is 1 ten. The 7 ones stay the same.

    $$57 \xrightarrow{-40} 17$$

    $57 - 41 = 16$

    > To subtract 41, I subtract 4 tens and then just subtract 1 one.

    $$57 \xrightarrow{-40} 17 \xrightarrow{-1} 16$$

    $57 - 39 = 18$

    > Subtracting 39 is subtracting 1 less than 40. I subtract 4 tens and then just add 1 one.

    $$57 \xrightarrow{-40} 17 \xrightarrow{+1} 18$$

    > The first problem, $57 - 40$, helps me solve the last problem, $57 - 39$. Subtracting 40 is easy, but that's 1 more than I'm supposed to take away, so I have to add 1 back, which means the answer is 18.

2. Solve using the arrow way, number bonds, or mental math.

$$43 + 20 = 63$$

$$\diagup \diagdown$$

40 3

> I can solve mentally, in my head! 20 more than 43 is 63. A number bond is another way I can show how I add like units.

©2015 Great Minds. eureka-math.org
G2-M1-HWH-1.3.0-07.2015

G2-M4-Lesson 4

1. Solve. Draw and label a tape diagram to subtract 10, 20, 30, 40, etc.

$23 - 9 = 24 - 10 = 14$

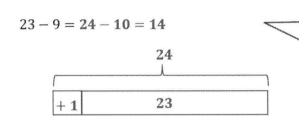

> It is easier to subtract a multiple of 10. 9 is very close to 10; it just needs 1 more. I can add 1 to both numbers to make it easier to subtract, and the difference will not change. A tape diagram helps me show my strategy.

2. Solve. Draw a number bond to add 10, 20, 30, 40, etc.

$38 + 53 = 40 + 51 = 91$

/ \
2 51

38	2	51

> It is easier to add a multiple of 10. 38 is very close to a 10, it just needs 2 more. I can break apart 53 into 2 and 51 to get the 2 out. 38 plus 2 is 40. Now I just add what is left; 40 plus 51 is 91.

> I can also show this with a tape diagram! This helps me see that if I take 2 from 53 and give it to 38, I get $40 + 51$.

G2-M4-Lesson 5

Solve and show your strategy.

1. There are 38 fewer green apples in the orchard than red apples. There are 62 green apples in the orchard. How many red apples are there?

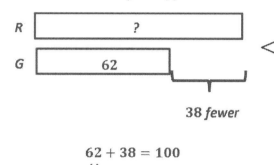

I use the RDW process to solve. After reading, I think about what I can draw that will help me solve. A tape diagram helps me see the parts that I know. I know there are 38 fewer green apples than red, so that means there are more red apples, 38 more. I add to find the number of red apples.

$$62 + 38 = 100$$
$$/\ \\$$
$$60 \quad 2$$

$$38 + 2 = 40$$
$$60 + 40 = 100$$

I used the make ten strategy to solve!

There are 100 red apples.

2. Oscar has two baskets of toys. The red basket has 27 toys. The yellow basket has 29 more toys than the red basket.

  a. How many toys are in the yellow basket?

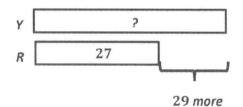

The yellow basket has 29 more than the red basket. I add to find 29 more than 27. I can use the make ten strategy here, too!

$$27 + 29 = 56$$
$$/\ \\$$
$$26 \quad 1$$

$$29 + 1 = 30$$
$$26 + 30 = 56$$

The yellow basket has 56 toys.

EUREKA
MATH

©2015 Great Minds. eureka-math.org
G2-M1-HWH-1.3.0-07.2015

b. Oscar gave 18 toys from the yellow basket to his younger brother. How many toys are left in the yellow basket?

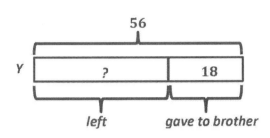

$56 - 18 = 38$

$/\,\backslash$

36 20 $20 - 18 = 2$

$36 + 2 = 38$

There are 38 toys left in the yellow basket.

EUREKA MATH   **Lesson 5:**   Solve one- and two-step word problems within 100 using strategies   7
based on place value.

©2015 Great Minds. eureka-math.org
G2-M1-HWH-1.3.0-07.2015

G2-M4-Lesson 6

1. Solve the following problems using your place value chart and place value disks. Compose a ten, if needed. Think about which ones you can solve mentally, too!

$34 + 25 = \underline{\ 59\ }$

> I can solve this one mentally! I just add like units. 3 tens and 2 tens is 5 tens. 4 ones and 5 ones is 9 ones. Altogether that makes 5 tens 9 ones, or 59.

$34 + 28 = \underline{\ 62\ }$

> I can use my chart and place value disks to solve this problem.

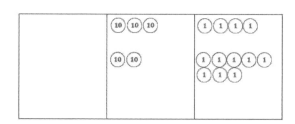

> I made a ten!

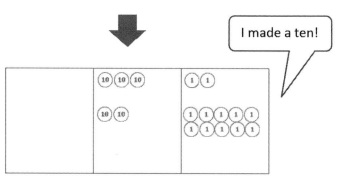

So, $34 + 28 = 62.$

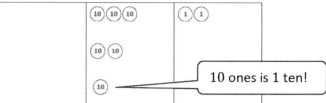

> 10 ones is 1 ten!

Lesson 6:   Use manipulatives to represent the composition of 10 ones as 1 ten with two-digit addends.

EUREKA
MATH™

2. Solve using a place value chart.

Marty used 28 toothpicks for his art project, and 37 were left in the box. How many toothpicks were there in all?

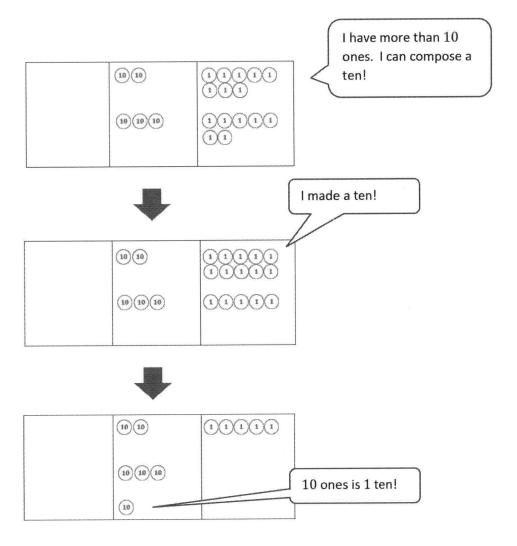

$28 + 37 = 65$

There were 65 toothpicks in all.

EUREKA MATH **Lesson 6:** Use manipulatives to represent the composition of 10 ones as 1 ten with two-digit addends.   9

©2015 Great Minds. eureka-math.org
G2-M1-HWH-1.3.0-07.2015

G2-M4-Lesson 7

1. Solve the following problems using the vertical form, your place value chart, and place value disks. Bundle a ten, if needed. Think about which ones you can solve mentally, too!

a. $33 + 7 = 40$

> I can solve this one mentally! I know 3 ones plus 7 ones is 1 ten, and 30 plus 10 is 40.

b. $36 + 57 = 93$

> I can use my chart and place value disks to solve.

> I can write it in vertical form as I model it with my place value disks.

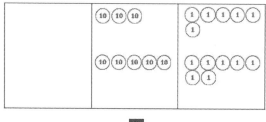

$$\begin{array}{r} 3\ 6 \\ +\ 5\ 7 \\ \hline \end{array}$$

I made a ten!

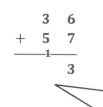

$$\begin{array}{r} 3\ 6 \\ +\ 5\ 7 \\ \underline{\ \ \ 1\ \ } \\ 3 \end{array}$$

> I have 13 ones, or 1 ten 3 ones. I show the ten, using new groups below, on the line below the tens place.

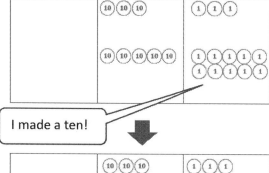

10 ones is 1 ten!

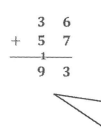

$$\begin{array}{r} 3\ 6 \\ +\ 5\ 7 \\ \underline{\ \ \ 1\ \ } \\ 9\ 3 \end{array}$$

> Now I just add the tens! 3 tens plus 5 tens is 8 tens, and 1 more ten is 9 tens. So 36 plus 57 is 93.

Lesson 7:   Relate addition using manipulatives to a written vertical method

EUREKA MATH

©2015 Great Minds. eureka-math.org
G2-M1-HWH-1.3.0-07.2015

2. Add the bottom numbers to find the missing number above it.

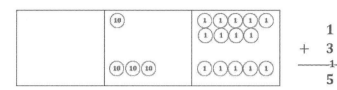

$$\begin{array}{r} 1\ 9 \\ +\ 3\ 5 \\ \hline {\scriptstyle 1} \\ 5\ 4 \end{array}$$

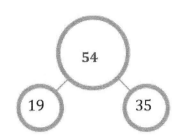

$19 + 35 = 54$
/ \
1 34

I can solve using my place value disks and vertical form or the make ten strategy!

3. Jen's ribbon is 18 centimeters longer than her desk. The length of her desk is 63 centimeters.

    a. What is the length of Jen's ribbon?

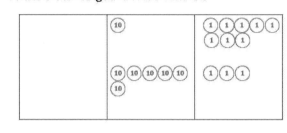

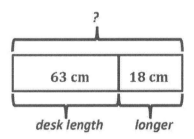

?

| 63 cm | 18 cm |

desk length   longer

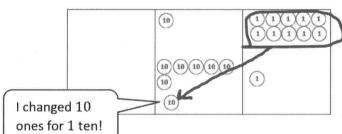

$$\begin{array}{r} 1\ 8 \\ +\ 6\ 3 \\ \hline {\scriptstyle 1} \\ 8\ 1 \end{array}$$

Jen's ribbon is 81 centimeters.

I changed 10 ones for 1 ten!

    b. The length of Jen's desk is 20 centimeters shorter than the length of her teacher's desk. How long is her teacher's desk?

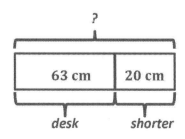

?

| 63 cm | 20 cm |

desk   shorter

$63 + 20 = 83$

The teacher's desk is 83 centimeters long.

G2-M4-Lesson 8

Solve vertically. Draw and bundle place value disks on the place value chart.

1. $27 + 45 = 72$

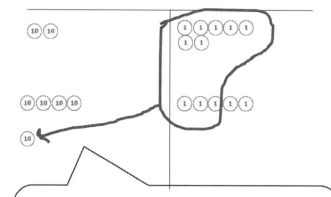

$$\begin{array}{r} 2\ 7 \\ +\ 4\ 5 \\ \scriptstyle 1 \\ \hline 7\ 2 \end{array}$$

> I show each step I make with the place value disks vertically using new groups below.

> I draw place value disks to show each addend. 7 ones plus 5 ones is 12 ones, or 1 ten 2 ones. I bundle 10 ones to make 1 ten. Now I just add the tens. 2 tens plus 4 tens plus 1 more ten is 7 tens. So 27 plus 45 is 72.

2. Santiago counted the number of people on two buses. Bus 1 had 29 people, and bus 2 had 34 people. How many people were on the two buses?

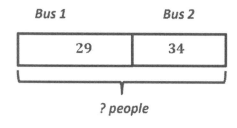

Bus 1 | Bus 2
29 | 34

? people

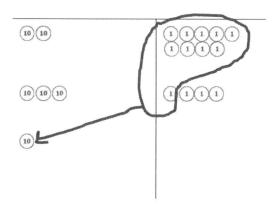

$$\begin{array}{r} 2\ 9 \\ +\ 3\ 4 \\ \scriptstyle 1 \\ \hline 6\ 3 \end{array}$$

63 people were on the two buses.

Lesson 8:   Use math drawings to represent the composition and relate drawings to a written method.

EUREKA MATH

G2-M4-Lesson 9

1. Solve using the algorithm. Draw and bundle chips on the place value chart.

$127 + 45 = 72$

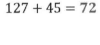

```
    1   2   7
+       4   5
    ─────────
        1
    1   7   2
```

I show each step I make with the chips vertically using new groups below.

hundreds	tens	ones

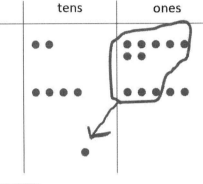

I draw chips to show each addend. 7 ones plus 5 ones is 12 ones, or 1 ten 2 ones. I bundle the 10 ones to make 1 ten. Now I just add the tens. 2 tens plus 4 tens plus 1 more ten is 7 tens. 1 hundred plus 0 hundreds is 1 hundred. So 127 plus 45 is 172.

2. Solve using the algorithm. Write a number sentence for the problem modeled on the place value chart.

hundreds	tens	ones

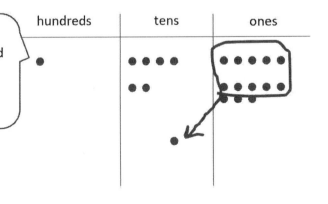

I can count to find the first addend: 100, 110, 120, 130, 140, 141, 142, 143, 144, 145. The first addend is 145. Now I count to find the second addend: 10, 20, 21, 22, 23, 24, 25, 26, 27, 28. The second addend is 28.

```
    1   4   5
+       2   8
    ─────────
        1
    1   7   3
```

EUREKA MATH™   Lesson 9:   Use math drawings to represent the composition when adding a   13
                            two-digit to a three-digit addend.

©2015 Great Minds. eureka-math.org
G2-M1-HWH-1.3.0-07.2015

G2-M4-Lesson 10

1. Solve using the algorithm. Draw and bundle chips on the place value chart.

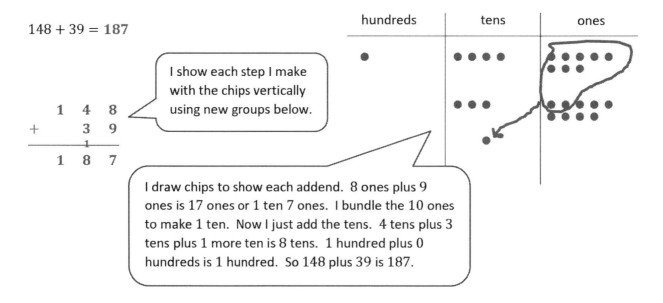

$148 + 39 = 187$

> I show each step I make with the chips vertically using new groups below.

```
    1   4   8
+       3   9
    ─────────
        1
    1   8   7
```

> I draw chips to show each addend. 8 ones plus 9 ones is 17 ones or 1 ten 7 ones. I bundle the 10 ones to make 1 ten. Now I just add the tens. 4 tens plus 3 tens plus 1 more ten is 8 tens. 1 hundred plus 0 hundreds is 1 hundred. So 148 plus 39 is 187.

hundreds	tens	ones

2. Frankie spilled ink on his paper. Can you figure out what problem he was given by looking at his work?

> I can count to find the first addend: 100, 110, 111, 112, 113, 114, 115. The first addend is 115. Now I can count to find the second addend: 10, 20, 30, 40, 50, 60, 70, 71, 72, 73, 74, 75, 76. The second addend is 76.

1 ⬤ = _____

__115__ + __76__ = __191__

hundreds	tens	ones

__1__ hundreds   __9__ tens   __1__ ones

©2015 Great Minds. eureka-math.org
G2-M1-HWH-1.3.0-07.2015

EUREKA MATH

G2-M4-Lesson 11

I can use $87 - 7$ to help me solve $87 - 8$. Since the difference in the first problem is 80, the difference in the second problem must be 1 less than 80 because I am only subtracting 1 more.

1. Solve using mental math.

$7 - 6 =$ ___1___ $87 - 6 =$ ___81___ $87 - 7 =$ ___80___ $87 - 8 =$ ___79___

2. Solve using your place value chart and place value disks. Unbundle a ten if needed. Think about which problems you can solve mentally, too!

   a. $28 - 7 =$ ___21___

   I can solve this one mentally! I can subtract 7 ones from 8 ones. That leaves 2 tens 1 one, 21.

   b. $28 - 9 =$ ___19___

   I can use my chart and place value disks to solve this problem.

   I only need to show 28 because I'm taking a part, 9, from the whole, 28.

   I can't subtract 9 ones from 8 ones, so I change 1 ten for 10 ones. Now I have 1 ten 18 ones, so I can subtract 9 ones.

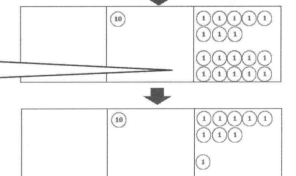

   So $28 - 9 = 19$.

EUREKA MATH

Lesson 11: Represent subtraction with and without the decomposition of 1 ten as 10 ones with manipulatives.

©2015 Great Minds. eureka-math.org
G2-M1-HWH-1.3.0-07.2015

15

3. Solve $56 - 28$, and explain your strategy.

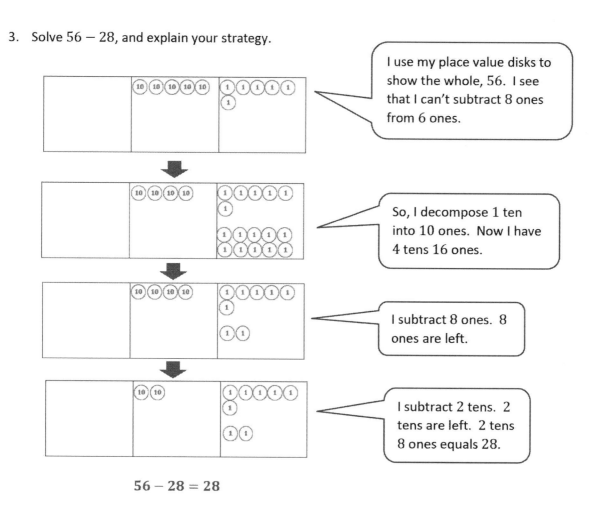

I use my place value disks to show the whole, 56. I see that I can't subtract 8 ones from 6 ones.

So, I decompose 1 ten into 10 ones. Now I have 4 tens 16 ones.

I subtract 8 ones. 8 ones are left.

I subtract 2 tens. 2 tens are left. 2 tens 8 ones equals 28.

$56 - 28 = 28$

4. The number of marbles in this jar is marked on the front. Miss Clark took 26 marbles out of the jar. How many marbles are left? Complete the number sentence to find out.

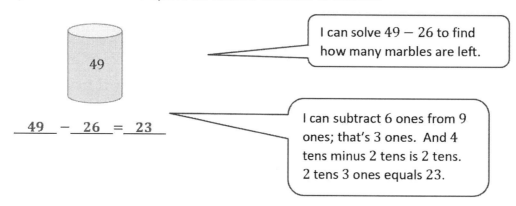

I can solve $49 - 26$ to find how many marbles are left.

$\underline{\ 49\ } - \underline{\ 26\ } = \underline{\ 23\ }$

I can subtract 6 ones from 9 ones; that's 3 ones. And 4 tens minus 2 tens is 2 tens. 2 tens 3 ones equals 23.

EUREKA
MATH™

G2-M4-Lesson 12

1. Use place value disks to solve the problem.
   Rewrite the problem vertically, and record each step.

   $71 - 27$

> I rewrite the problem in vertical form. Like a detective, I have to look carefully at the whole when subtracting, so I draw a magnifying glass around 71 to see if I need to do any unbundling.

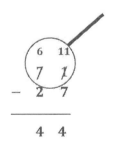

> What I do with the disks, I need to do in vertical form.

> I show the whole, 71, with my place value disks. I don't show 27 because it's already inside 71. When I subtract the part I know, 27, I'll find the missing part.

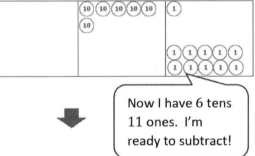

> I can't subtract 7 ones from 1 one, so I need to decompose, or unbundle, a ten.

> Now I have 6 tens 11 ones. I'm ready to subtract!

> 11 ones − 7 ones = 4 ones.
> 6 tens − 2 tens = 4 tens.
> 4 tens 4 ones is 44.

©2015 Great Minds. eureka-math.org
G2-M1-HWH-1.3.0-07.2015

2. Some Grade 1 and Grade 2 students voted on their favorite fruit. The table shows the number of votes for each fruit.

Types of Fruit	Number of Votes
Pineapple	26
Mango	18
Apple	15
Orange	35
Peach	43

a. How many more students voted for orange than pineapple? Show your work.

> I can't take 6 ones from 5 ones, so I unbundle 1 ten. Now I have 2 tens 15 ones.
>
> 15 ones − 6 ones = 9 ones.

> The tape diagram helps me see that I'm looking for the difference between 35 and 26. I can subtract using the vertical form to find the answer.

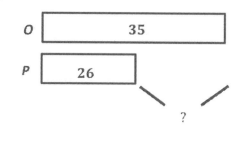

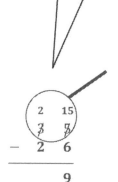

$35 - 26 = ?$

9 more students voted for orange than for pineapple.

b. How many fewer students voted for mango than for pineapple? Show your work.

> The tape diagram helps me see that I'm looking for the difference between 18 and 26.

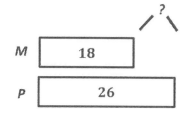

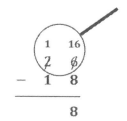

$26 - 18 = ?$

8 fewer students voted for mango than for pineapple.

18   Lesson 12:   Relate manipulative representations to a written method.   EUREKA MATH

©2015 Great Minds. eureka-math.org
G2-M1-HWH-1.3.0-07.2015

G2-M4-Lesson 13

Solve vertically. Draw a place value chart and chips to model each problem. Show how you change 1 ten for 10 ones, when necessary.

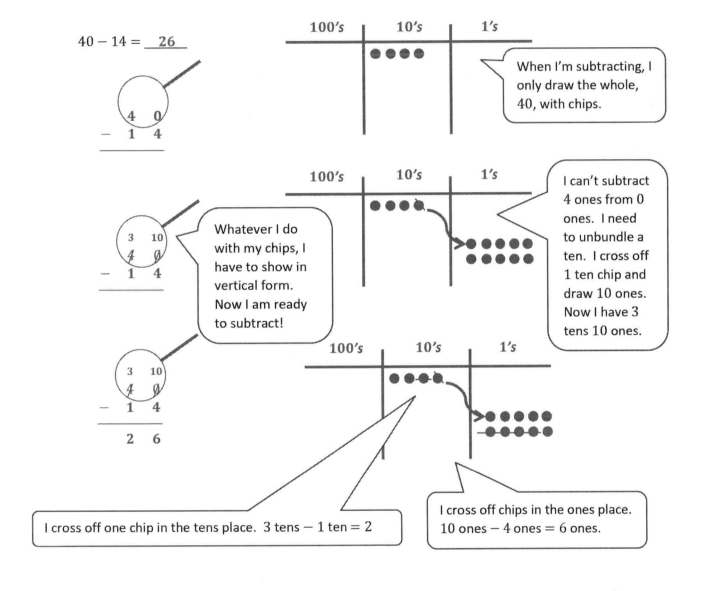

$40 - 14 = \underline{\ 26\ }$

When I'm subtracting, I only draw the whole, 40, with chips.

Whatever I do with my chips, I have to show in vertical form. Now I am ready to subtract!

I can't subtract 4 ones from 0 ones. I need to unbundle a ten. I cross off 1 ten chip and draw 10 ones. Now I have 3 tens 10 ones.

I cross off one chip in the tens place. 3 tens − 1 ten = 2

I cross off chips in the ones place. 10 ones − 4 ones = 6 ones.

EUREKA MATH   Lesson 13:   Use math drawings to represent subtraction with and without decompositions and relate drawings to a written method.   19

©2015 Great Minds. eureka-math.org
G2-M1-HWH-1.3.0-07.2015

G2-M4-Lesson 14

1. Solve by writing the problem vertically. Check your result by drawing chips on the place value chart. Change 1 ten for 10 ones, when needed.

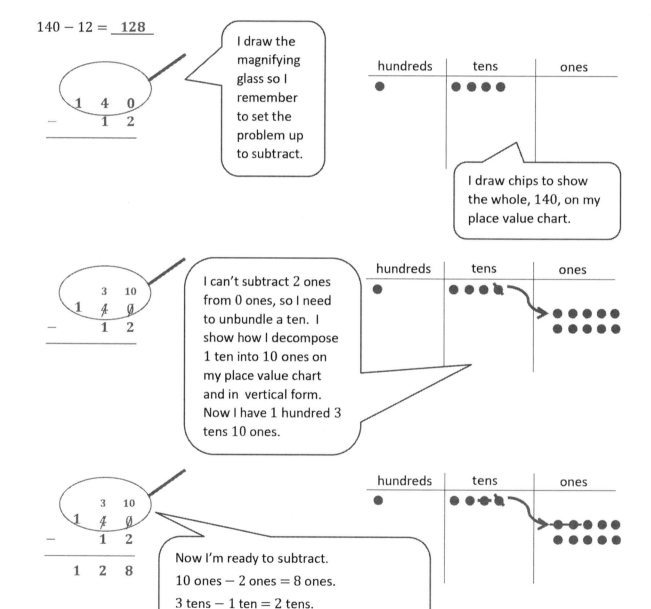

$140 - 12 = \underline{\ 128\ }$

I draw the magnifying glass so I remember to set the problem up to subtract.

I draw chips to show the whole, 140, on my place value chart.

I can't subtract 2 ones from 0 ones, so I need to unbundle a ten. I show how I decompose 1 ten into 10 ones on my place value chart and in vertical form. Now I have 1 hundred 3 tens 10 ones.

Now I'm ready to subtract.

10 ones − 2 ones = 8 ones.

3 tens − 1 ten = 2 tens.

1 hundred − 0 hundreds = 1 hundred.

1 hundred 2 tens 8 ones is 128.

Lesson 14:   Represent subtraction with and without the decomposition when there is a three-digit minuend.

EUREKA MATH

©2015 Great Minds. eureka-math.org
G2-M1-HWH-1.3.0-07.2015

2. Solve and show your work. Draw a place value chart and chips, if needed.

    a.   Ana has 173 marbles. She has 27 more than Rico. How many marbles does Rico have?

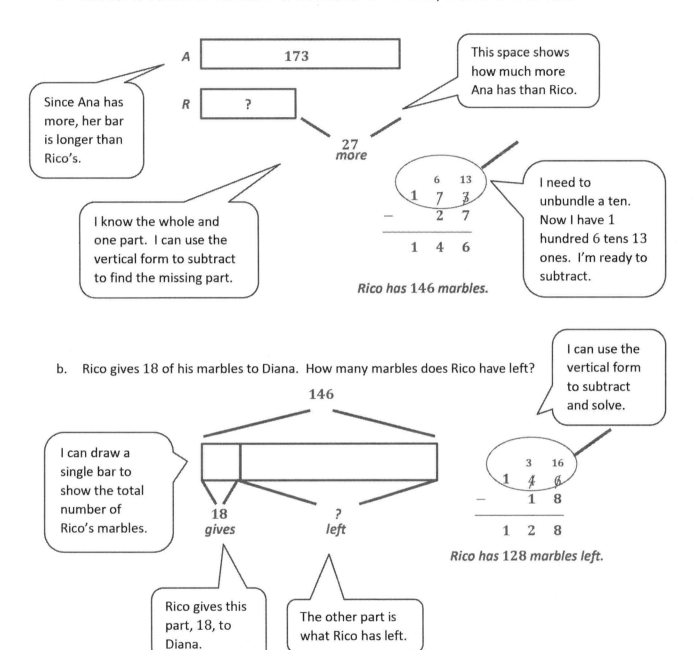

    b.   Rico gives 18 of his marbles to Diana. How many marbles does Rico have left?

G2-M4-Lesson 15

1. Solve using the vertical form. Show the subtraction on the place value chart with chips. Exchange 1 ten for 10 ones, if necessary.

$181 - 73$

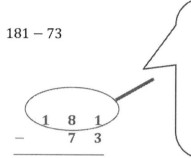

> Before I begin subtracting in vertical form, I have to get ready to subtract. I need to check each place to be sure I have enough!

hundreds	tens	ones
●	●●●●● ●●●	●

> I don't have enough ones in the ones place.

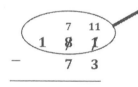

> I unbundle a ten as 10 ones. I remember to show this change in vertical form.

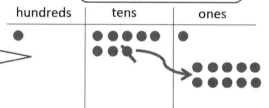

hundreds	tens	ones

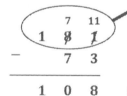

> I'm ready to subtract.
> 11 ones − 3 ones = 8 ones.
> 7 tens −7 tens = 0 tens.
> 1 hundred − 0 hundreds = 1 hundred.
> 1 hundred 8 ones is 108.

hundreds	tens	ones

Lesson 15:   Represent subtraction with and without the decomposition when there is a three-digit minuend.

EUREKA MATH

2. Maya solved 157 − 39 vertically and on her place value chart. Explain what Maya did correctly and what she needs to fix.

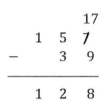

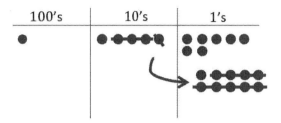

a. Maya correctly *models the problem on the place value chart. She shows the whole, 157, and*

    then she decomposes 1 ten as 10 ones. She changes the model to show 1 hundred 4 tens 17

    ones. After she crosses off 3 tens 9 ones, the model shows the correct answer, 118.

b. Maya needs to fix *the vertical form. She forgot to draw the magnifying glass, which would*

    have reminded her to look carefully to set the problem up for subtraction. She didn't show the

    change in the tens place, so she subtracted 3 tens from 5 tens, instead of subtracting from 4

    tens. That's why she got the wrong answer, 128.

EUREKA
MATH™

Lesson 15:   Represent subtraction with and without the decomposition when there   23
              is a three-digit minuend.

©2015 Great Minds. eureka-math.org
G2-M1-HWH-1.3.0-07.2015

G2-M4-Lesson 16

Solve the following word problems. Use the RDW process.

1. Audrey put 56 beads on a necklace. Some beads fell off, but she still has 28 left. How many beads fell off?

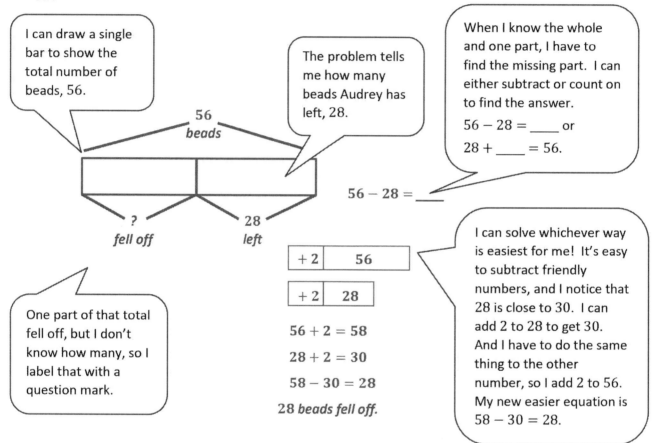

I can draw a single bar to show the total number of beads, 56.

The problem tells me how many beads Audrey has left, 28.

When I know the whole and one part, I have to find the missing part. I can either subtract or count on to find the answer.

$56 - 28 =$ _____ or

$28 +$ _____ $= 56$.

$56 - 28 =$ _____

One part of that total fell off, but I don't know how many, so I label that with a question mark.

| + 2 | 56 |
| + 2 | 28 |

$56 + 2 = 58$

$28 + 2 = 30$

$58 - 30 = 28$

28 beads fell off.

I can solve whichever way is easiest for me! It's easy to subtract friendly numbers, and I notice that 28 is close to 30. I can add 2 to 28 to get 30. And I have to do the same thing to the other number, so I add 2 to 56. My new easier equation is $58 - 30 = 28$.

2. Farmer Ben picks 87 apples. 26 apples are green, 20 are yellow, and the rest are red. How many apples are red?

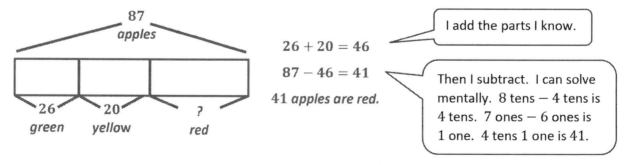

$26 + 20 = 46$

$87 - 46 = 41$

41 apples are red.

I add the parts I know.

Then I subtract. I can solve mentally. 8 tens − 4 tens is 4 tens. 7 ones − 6 ones is 1 one. 4 tens 1 one is 41.

EUREKA
MATH™

3. Ava planted 45 flowers in the morning. She planted 26 fewer flowers in the afternoon. How many flowers did she plant altogether?

> I draw and label how many flowers Ava planted in the morning.

> But I do know how many fewer she planted in the afternoon, so I can label this space.

M [45]

> I know she planted fewer flowers in the afternoon, but I don't know how many, so I draw a shorter bar and label it with a question mark.

A [?]

26
fewer

> To find how many flowers Ava planted in the afternoon, I can subtract the part, 26, from the whole, 45.

$$45 - 26 = \underline{\quad}$$

> I can use the chip model and vertical form to solve.

$$
\begin{array}{r}
3\ \ 15 \\
\cancel{4}\ \ \cancel{5} \\
-\ \ 2\ \ 6 \\
\hline
1\ \ 9
\end{array}
$$

tens | ones

Ava planted 19 flowers in the afternoon.

> To find out how many flowers Ava planted altogether, I add the parts, 45 and 19.

45   19
  ?

> I can use another model to show my work. The number bond shows that I know the two parts. I need to find the whole.

$$45 + 19 = \underline{\ 64\ }$$
/ \
44   1

> I can use the make ten strategy because 19 is close to 20. I break apart 45 into 44 and 1. Then it's easy!
> $44 + 20 = 64$, so $45 + 19 = 64$.

Ava planted 64 flowers altogether.

Lesson 16:   Solve one- and two-step word problems within 100 using strategies based on place value.

©2015 Great Minds. eureka-math.org
G2-M1-HWH-1.3.0-07.2015

25

G2-M4-Lesson 17

1. Solve mentally.

> I have to pay attention to the unit. 8 tens equal 80. 1 hundred more than 80 is 180.

1 ten more than 8 ones = __18__ $10 + 8 =$ __18__

1 hundred more than 8 ones = __108__ $100 + 8 =$ __108__

1 hundred more than 8 tens = __180__ $100 + 80 =$ __180__

12 ones + 2 ones = __1__ ten(s) __4__ one(s) $12 + 2 =$ __14__

12 tens + 2 tens = __1__ hundred(s) __4__ tens(s) $120 + 20 =$ __140__

> Both of these number sentences show 12 + 2. What's different is the unit. Adding 10 ones makes 1 ten. Adding 10 tens makes 1 hundred.

2. Solve.

7 ones + 8 ones = __1__ ten __5__ ones $7 + 8 =$ __15__

7 tens + 8 tens = __1__ hundred __5__ tens $70 + 80 =$ __150__

> 15 tens is the same as 150. I can show 15 tens on a place value chart. When I circle 10 tens, I make a hundred, and there are 5 tens left.

3. Fill in the blanks. Then, complete the addition sentence.

$$54 \xrightarrow{+6} \underline{\ 60\ } \xrightarrow{+40} \underline{\ 100\ } \xrightarrow{+10} \underline{\ 110\ } \xrightarrow{+10} \underline{\ 120\ } \xrightarrow{+100} \underline{\ 220\ }$$

$54 +$ __166__ $=$ __220__

> First, I add 6 to make a ten, 60. Then I add 40 to make a hundred. It's easy to add on 2 more tens and a hundred to make 220.

Lesson 17:   Use mental strategies to relate compositions of 10 tens as 1 hundred to 10 ones as 1 ten.   **EUREKA MATH**

©2015 Great Minds. eureka-math.org
G2-M1-HWH-1.3.0-07.2015

G2-M4-Lesson 18

> These problems are very similar. Just from looking at the tens and ones, I know that my second answer will have 1 more ten and 1 more one than the first answer.

1. Solve using your place value chart and place value disks.

   $35 + 76 =$ __111__ $36 + 86 =$ __122__

   > 36 is one more than 35, and 86 is 10 more than 76.

2. Circle the statements that are true as you solve the problem using place value disks.

   $136 + 58$

   (I change 10 ones for 1 ten.)

   I change 10 tens for 1 hundred.

   The total of the two parts is 184.

   (The total of the two parts is 194.)

   > I can set up this problem with place value disks and add like units. 6 ones and 8 ones are 14 ones. I can change 10 ones for 1 ten. I'll have 4 ones left over. Then, 3 tens + 5 tens + 1 ten equals 9 tens. 1 hundred + 9 tens + 4 ones = 194.

3. Solve the problem using your place value disks, and fill in the missing total. Then, write an addition sentence that relates to the number bond.

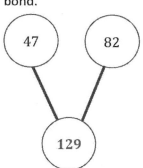

   > I can change 10 tens for 1 hundred!

   > I have 9 ones. I can't make a ten.

   > Now I have 1 hundred 2 tens 9 ones, 129.

   Addition sentence:

   $47 + 82 = 129$

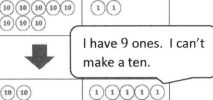

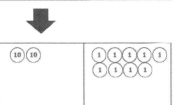

G2-M4-Lesson 19

1. Solve the following problems using the vertical form, your place value chart, and place value disks. Bundle a ten or hundred, if needed.

> I can solve this one mentally! 69 is close to 70, so I can think $24 + 70 = 94$. Then, I can just subtract 1, and the answer is 93.

a. $24 + 69 = \underline{\ 93\ }$

b. $137 + 63 = \underline{200}$

> I can use my chart and place value disks to solve.

> I write it in vertical form as I model it with my place value disks.

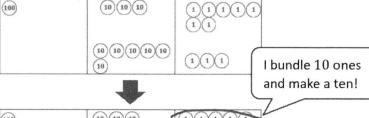

$$
\begin{array}{r}
1\ \ 3\ \ 7 \\
+\ \ \ \ \ 6\ \ 3 \\
\hline
\end{array}
$$

> I bundle 10 ones and make a ten!

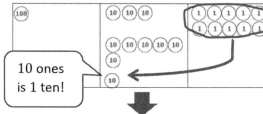

> 10 ones is 1 ten!

> I show the ten using new groups below, on the line below the tens place.

$$
\begin{array}{r}
1\ \ 3\ \ 7 \\
+\ \ \ \ \ 6\ \ 3 \\
\hline
{}_{1} \\
0
\end{array}
$$

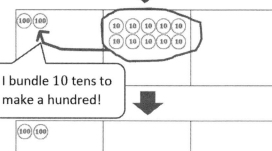

> I bundle 10 tens to make a hundred!

$$
\begin{array}{r}
1\ \ 3\ \ 7 \\
+\ \ \ \ \ 6\ \ 3 \\
\hline
{}_{1}\ \ {}_{1} \\
0\ \ 0
\end{array}
$$

> Now I add the tens. 3 tens plus 6 tens plus 1 ten is 10 tens. I can bundle again to make 1 hundred! I show the hundred using new groups below again.

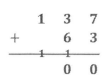

$$
\begin{array}{r}
1\ \ 3\ \ 7 \\
+\ \ \ \ \ 6\ \ 3 \\
\hline
{}_{1}\ \ {}_{1} \\
2\ \ 0\ \ 0
\end{array}
$$

> Last, I add the hundreds. There are 2 hundreds.

EUREKA MATH™

ty-nine more boys attended than girls.

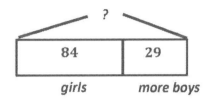

girls more boys

ce value
dition
show
and

I can draw a tape diagram to represent the story. I can use the make ten strategy to solve! (See below.)

84 + 29 = _____

83   1

83 + 30 = 113

b. How many boys and girls attended swim school?

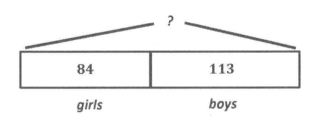

girls   boys

197 *boys and girls attended swim school.*

```
  1 1 3
+   8 4
-------
  1 9 7
```

Now that I know the number of boys, I can add the girls and boys together to find the total. I can show my work using the vertical method.

G2-M4-Lesson 20

Solve vertically. Draw chips on the place value chart and bundle, when needed.

1. $58 + 74 =$ __132__

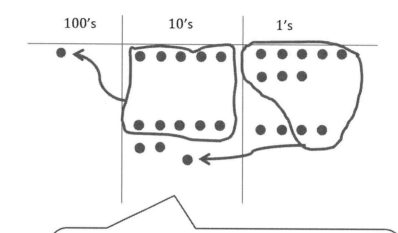

$$\begin{array}{r} 5 \ 8 \\ + \quad 7 \ 4 \\ \tiny 1 \ \ 1 \\ \hline 1 \ 3 \ 2 \end{array}$$

I show each step I make with chips vertically using new groups below.

I draw chips to show each addend. 8 ones plus 4 ones is 12 ones, or 1 ten 2 ones. I bundle 10 ones to make 1 ten. Now I add the tens. 5 tens plus 7 tens plus 1 more ten is 13 tens. I can bundle again! 10 tens makes 1 hundred. So, 13 tens is 1 hundred 3 tens.

2. For the box below, find and circle two numbers that add up to 160.

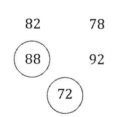

82   78

(88)   92

(72)

If I add 88 and 72, I can add 8 ones and 2 ones, which is 10 ones. I can bundle ten ones to make 1 ten! Then, I can add 8 tens plus 7 tens plus 1 ten to get 16 tens, or 160.

I see the trap; if I forgot to add another ten, I might have chosen 88 and 82 or 78 and 92.

Lesson 20:   Use math drawings to represent additions with up to two compositions and relate drawings to a written method.

EUREKA
MATH™

G2-M4-Lesson 21

Solve vertically. Draw chips on the place value chart and bundle, when needed.

1. $138 + 62 =$ __200__

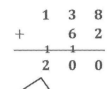

$$
\begin{array}{r}
1\ 3\ 8 \\
+\quad 6\ 2 \\
\hline
1\ 1 \\
\hline
2\ 0\ 0
\end{array}
$$

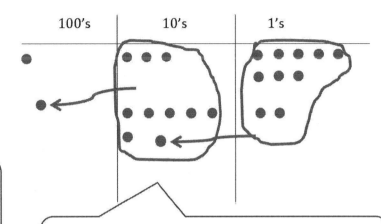

100's   10's   1's

My model matches the vertical method. I bundled twice, and I can show the new units with new groups below.

Renaming the tens is just like renaming ones. I have to look for 10 of a unit to make the next higher value unit. So, 10 ones make 1 ten, and 10 tens make 1 hundred!

2. The orange team scored 26 fewer points than the green team. The orange team scored 49 points.

   a. How many points did the green team score?

I can draw a comparison tape diagram to solve.

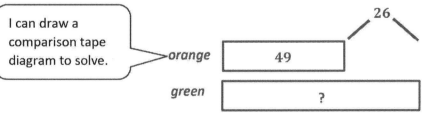

26

orange | 49 |

green | ? |

$49 + 26 =$ __?__

$50 + 26 = 76$

$76 - 1 = 75$

The green team scored 75 points.

I don't need to solve with chips because 49 is close to 50. I can add 50 and 26, which makes 76. Then, I can subtract 1 since 49 is 1 less than 50. I can use the same strategy for Part (b).

EUREKA MATH™

Lesson 21:   Use math drawings to represent additions with up to two compositions and relate drawings to a written method.

31

©2015 Great Minds. eureka-math.org
G2-M1-HWH-1.3.0-07.2015

b.   How many points did the orange and green teams score altogether?

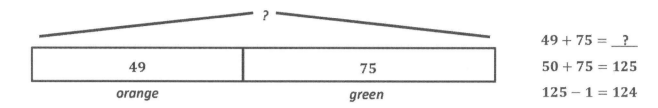

$49 + 75 = $ __?__

$50 + 75 = 125$

$125 - 1 = 124$

The orange and green team scored 124 points altogether.

Lesson 21:   Use math drawings to represent additions with up to two compositions
and relate drawings to a written method.

©2015 Great Minds. eureka-math.org
G2-M1-HWH-1.3.0-07.2015

**EUREKA
MATH**

G2-M4-Lesson 22

1. Look to make 10 ones or 10 tens to solve the following problems using place value strategies.

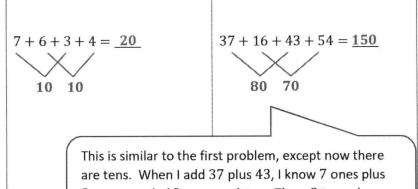

$7 + 6 + 3 + 4 =$ __20__

10   10

$37 + 16 + 43 + 54 =$ __150__

80   70

$86 + 34 + 33 + 67 =$ __220__

120   100

This is similar to the first problem, except now there are tens. When I add 37 plus 43, I know 7 ones plus 3 ones equals 10 ones, or 1 ten. Then, 3 tens plus 4 tens equals 7 tens. 7 tens + 1 ten = 8 tens, or 80.

I can group 86 and 34 together because 6 and 4 make 10. 8 tens plus 3 tens equals 11 tens. When I add 1 more ten, I get 12 tens, which is 120. $120 + 100 = 220$.

2. The table shows the top five soccer teams and their total points scored this season.

Teams	Points
Red	48
Yellow	39
Green	52
Blue	41
Orange	42

a. How many points did the yellow, orange, and blue teams score together?

$39 + 42 + 41 =$ __122__

80 + 42

Since 9 and 1 make ten, I added 39 and 41 first. I know that $30 + 40 = 70$, and $70 + 10 = 80$. Then, $80 + 42 = 122$.

The yellow, orange, and blue teams scored 122 points.

©2015 Great Minds. eureka-math.org
G2-M1-HWH-1.3.0-07.2015

b. Which two teams scored a total of 90 points?

$$48 + 42 = 90$$

The red and orange teams scored 90 points.

> I can look for a total of 9 tens. 4 tens plus 4 tens is 8 tens, which is only 80. But, don't forget the ones! 8 ones plus 2 ones equals 10 ones, or 1 ten. So 8 tens and 1 more ten is 9 tens, or 90.

Lesson 22: Solve additions with up to four addends with totals within 200 with and without two compositions of larger units.

©2015 Great Minds. eureka-math.org
G2-M1-HWH-1.3.0-07.2015

EUREKA MATH

G2-M4-Lesson 23

1. Solve using number bonds to subtract from 100.

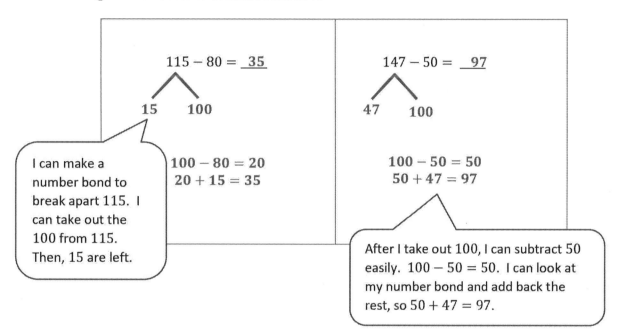

$$115 - 80 = \underline{\ 35\ }$$

15   100

I can make a
number bond to
break apart 115. I
can take out the
100 from 115.
Then, 15 are left.

$$100 - 80 = 20$$
$$20 + 15 = 35$$

$$147 - 50 = \underline{\ 97\ }$$

47   100

$$100 - 50 = 50$$
$$50 + 47 = 97$$

After I take out 100, I can subtract 50
easily. $100 - 50 = 50$. I can look at
my number bond and add back the
rest, so $50 + 47 = 97$.

2. Jana sold 60 fewer candles than Charlotte. Charlotte sold 132 candles. How many candles did Jana sell?
Solve using a number bond.

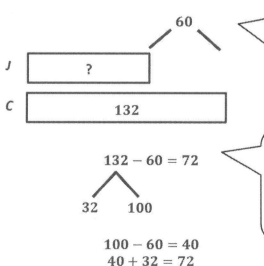

60

J   [?]

C   [132]

My tape diagram shows that I
don't know how many candles
Jana sold, but I know that
Charlotte sold 60 more candles
than Jana.

$$132 - 60 = 72$$

32   100

I can break apart 132 so I can subtract
from the hundred. This is a good strategy
since it's easy to solve $100 - 60 = 40$.
Then, I can add back the other part, so
$40 + 32 = 72$.

$$100 - 60 = 40$$
$$40 + 32 = 72$$

Jana sold 72 candles.

**EUREKA
MATH**™   **Lesson 23:**   Use number bonds to break apart three-digit minuends and subtract
                        from the hundred   35

©2015 Great Minds. eureka-math.org
G2-M1-HWH-1.3.0-07.2015

G2-M4-Lesson 24

1. Solve using mental math. If you cannot solve mentally, use your place value chart and place value disks.

    $47 - 7 =$ __40__ $47 - 8 =$ __39__ $147 - 47 =$ __100__ $147 - 48 =$ __99__

    > I can use $147 - 47$ to help me solve $147 - 48$. Since the difference in the first problem is 100, the difference in the second problem must be 1 less than 100 because I am only subtracting 1 more.

2. Solve using your place value chart and place value disks. Unbundle the hundred or ten when necessary. Circle what you did to model each problem.

    $145 - 87 =$ __58__

    I unbundled the hundred.   (Yes) No

    I unbundled a ten.   (Yes) No

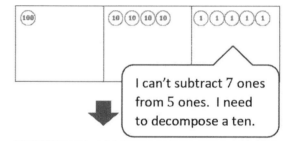

> I can't subtract 7 ones from 5 ones. I need to decompose a ten.

> I only have 3 tens. That's not enough to subtract 8 tens! I need to unbundle the hundred.

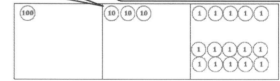

> Now I have 15 ones. That's enough to subtract 7 ones.

> Now I have 13 tens and 15 ones. I am ready to subtract!
> 13 tens $-$ 8 tens $=$ 5 tens.
> 15 ones $-$ 7 ones $=$ 8 ones.
> 5 tens 8 ones is 58.

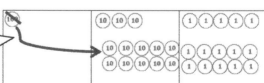

36   **Lesson 24:**   Use manipulatives to represent subtraction with decompositions of
                                1 hundred as 10 tens and 1 ten as 10 ones.

©2015 Great Minds. eureka-math.org
G2-M1-HWH-1.3.0-07.2015

EUREKA
MATH™

3. 76 pencils in the basket are sharpened. The basket has 132 pencils. How many pencils are not sharpened?

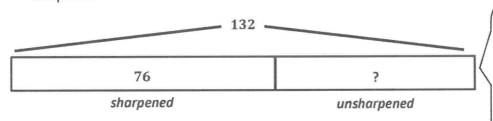

132

76	?
sharpened	*unsharpened*

My tape diagram shows that 132 is the total. I know that one part is 76 sharpened pencils. I am solving for the number of pencils that are not sharpened. That's my unknown.

$$132 - 76 = ?$$

$$76 \xrightarrow{+4} 80 \xrightarrow{+20} 100 \xrightarrow{+32} 132$$

56 pencils are not sharpened.

I can use the arrow way to find the missing part. I can start at 76 and add 4 to get to a friendly number, 80. Then, I can add 20 to get to 1 hundred. Then, 32 more is 132. So, $20 + 32 + 4 = 56$.

EUREKA MATH
   Lesson 24:   Use manipulatives to represent subtraction with decompositions of 1 hundred as 10 tens and 1 ten as 10 ones.   37

©2015 Great Minds. eureka-math.org
G2-M1-HWH-1.3.0-07.2015

G2-M4-Lesson 25

1. Solve the following problems using the vertical form, your place value chart, and place value disks. Unbundle a ten or hundred when necessary. Show your work for each problem.

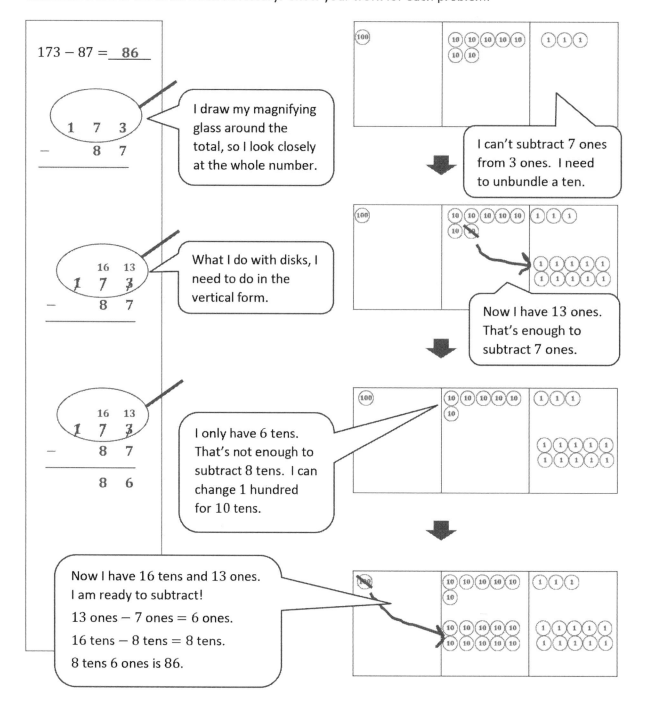

EUREKA
MATH

©2015 Great Minds. eureka-math.org
G2-M1-HWH-1.3.0-07.2015

2. Vazyl has $127. He has $65 more than Sergio. How much money does Sergio have?

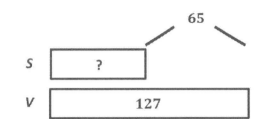

$127 - 65 = ?$

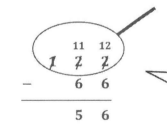

I can use the vertical method to figure out how much money Sergio has. I only have to unbundle the hundred because there are enough ones to subtract.

7 ones − 5 ones = 2 ones.

12 tens − 6 tens = 6 tens.

6 tens 2 ones is 62.

Sergio has 62 dollars.

3. Which problem will have the same answer as $122 - 66$? Show your work.

a. $144 - 55$

b. $126 - 62$

c. $166 - 22$

d. $144 - 88$

I can use the vertical form to solve $122 - 66$.

But I also know another strategy. If I add 22 to both numbers, the difference doesn't change. So, $122 + 22 = 144$. And $66 + 22 = 88$. That means $144 - 88 = 56$. I remember this; it's called compensation!

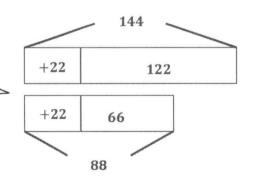

G2-M4-Lesson 26

Solve vertically. Draw chips on the place value chart. Unbundle when needed.

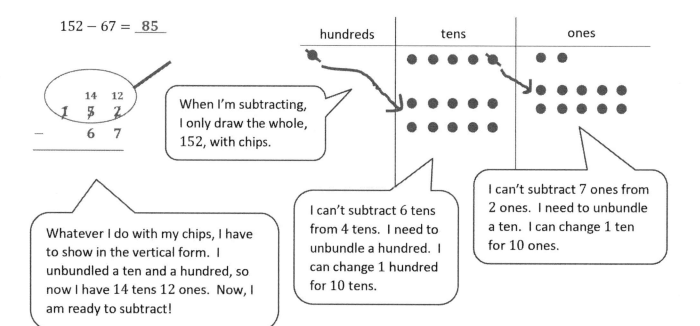

$152 - 67 = \underline{85}$

When I'm subtracting, I only draw the whole, 152, with chips.

Whatever I do with my chips, I have to show in the vertical form. I unbundled a ten and a hundred, so now I have 14 tens 12 ones. Now, I am ready to subtract!

I can't subtract 6 tens from 4 tens. I need to unbundle a hundred. I can change 1 hundred for 10 tens.

I can't subtract 7 ones from 2 ones. I need to unbundle a ten. I can change 1 ten for 10 ones.

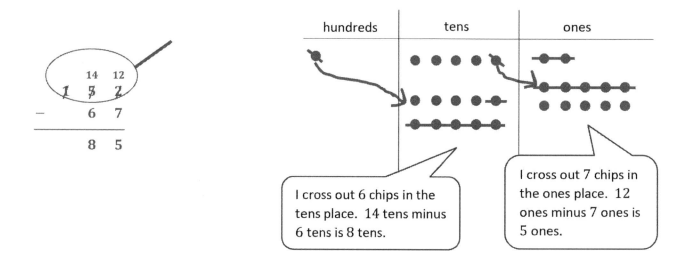

I cross out 6 chips in the tens place. 14 tens minus 6 tens is 8 tens.

I cross out 7 chips in the ones place. 12 ones minus 7 ones is 5 ones.

Lesson 26:   Use math drawings to relate subtraction with up to two decompositions and relate drawings to a written method.

EUREKA
MATH

G2-M4-Lesson 27

Solve vertically. Draw chips on the place value chart. Unbundle when needed.

$200 - 66 = \underline{134}$

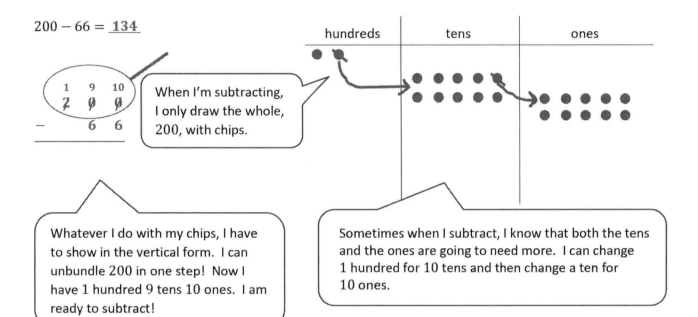

When I'm subtracting, I only draw the whole, 200, with chips.

Whatever I do with my chips, I have to show in the vertical form. I can unbundle 200 in one step! Now I have 1 hundred 9 tens 10 ones. I am ready to subtract!

Sometimes when I subtract, I know that both the tens and the ones are going to need more. I can change 1 hundred for 10 tens and then change a ten for 10 ones.

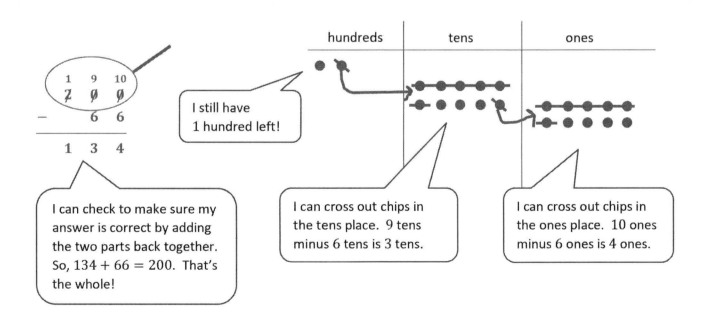

I still have 1 hundred left!

I can check to make sure my answer is correct by adding the two parts back together. So, $134 + 66 = 200$. That's the whole!

I can cross out chips in the tens place. 9 tens minus 6 tens is 3 tens.

I can cross out chips in the ones place. 10 ones minus 6 ones is 4 ones.

G2-M4-Lesson 28

1. Solve vertically. Draw chips on the place value chart. Unbundle when needed.

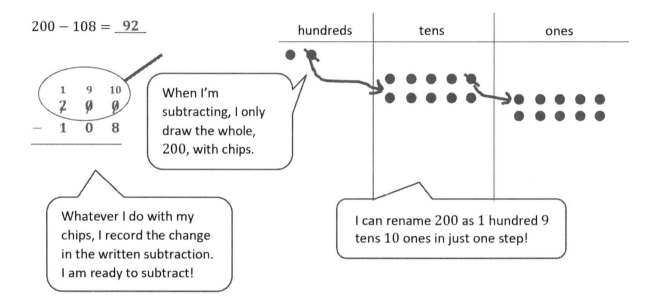

$200 - 108 = \underline{92}$

When I'm subtracting, I only draw the whole, 200, with chips.

I can rename 200 as 1 hundred 9 tens 10 ones in just one step!

Whatever I do with my chips, I record the change in the written subtraction. I am ready to subtract!

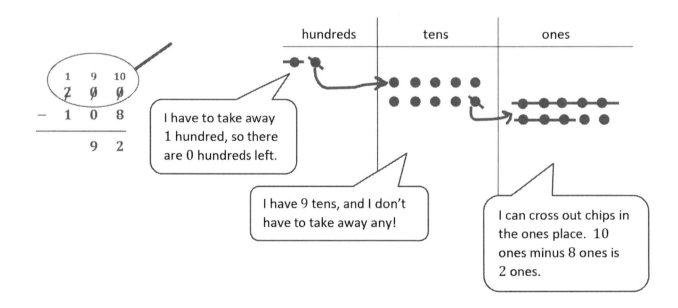

I have to take away 1 hundred, so there are 0 hundreds left.

I have 9 tens, and I don't have to take away any!

I can cross out chips in the ones place. 10 ones minus 8 ones is 2 ones.

EUREKA MATH

2. Harry collected 200 baseball cards. He traded 127 of them and kept the rest. How many baseball cards did he keep?

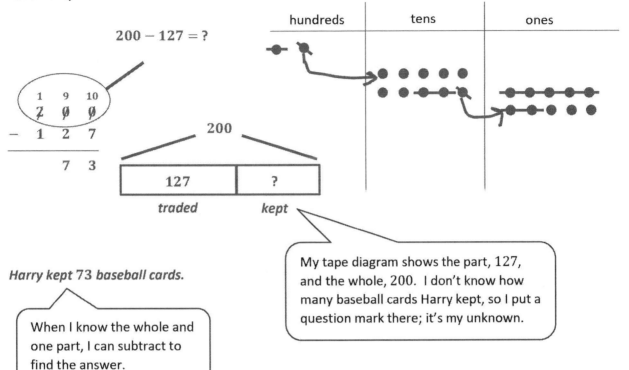

$$200 - 127 = ?$$

Harry kept 73 baseball cards.

When I know the whole and one part, I can subtract to find the answer.

My tape diagram shows the part, 127, and the whole, 200. I don't know how many baseball cards Harry kept, so I put a question mark there; it's my unknown.

G2-M4-Lesson 29

1. Add like units, and record the totals below.

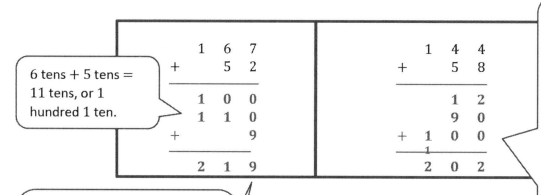

6 tens + 5 tens = 11 tens, or 1 hundred 1 ten.

```
    1  6  7
 +     5  2
 ─────────────
    1  0  0
    1  1  0
 +        9
 ─────────────
    2  1  9
```

```
    1  4  4
 +     5  8
 ─────────────
       1  2
       9  0
 +  1  0  0
    1
 ─────────────
    2  0  2
```

I add all the ones, tens, and hundreds. Look, there are 10 tens! That's the same as 1 hundred 0 tens. I record the hundred on the line.

Here, I add the hundreds, then tens, and then ones. If I added starting with the ones, the totals would still be the same because I am adding the same parts!

2. Dana counted 59 peaches on one tree and 87 peaches on another tree. How many peaches were on both trees? Add like units and record the totals below to solve.

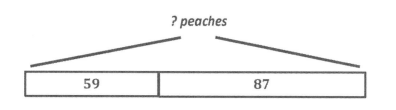

? peaches

| 59 | 87 |

```
       5  9
 +     8  7
 ─────────────
    1  3  0
 +     1  6
 ─────────────
    1  4  6
```

146 *peaches were on both trees.*

Lesson 29:   Use and explain the totals below method using words, math drawings, and numbers.

©2015 Great Minds. eureka-math.org
G2-M1-HWH-1.3.0-07.2015

EUREKA MATH

G2-M4-Lesson 30

1. Linda and Keith solved $127 + 59$.

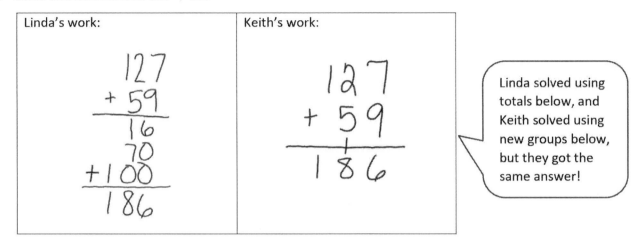

Linda's work:	Keith's work:

Linda solved using totals below, and Keith solved using new groups below, but they got the same answer!

Explain what is different about how Linda and Keith solved the problem.

Linda added the ones, tens, and hundreds by themselves to get the 3 parts: 16, 70, and 100. Then, she added those parts up to get 186. Keith renamed 16 ones as 1 ten 6 ones. Next, he added 2 tens plus 5 tens plus 1 ten, which equals 8 tens. Then, he added 1 hundred. They got the same answer!

2. Here is one way to solve $124 + 69$. Solve $124 + 69$ another way.

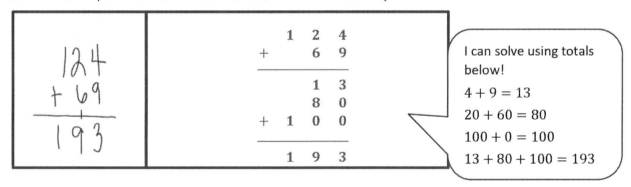

I can solve using totals below!
$4 + 9 = 13$
$20 + 60 = 80$
$100 + 0 = 100$
$13 + 80 + 100 = 193$

Explain how the two ways to solve $124 + 69$ are similar.

In the first problem, when you rename 13 ones, you can see that 1 hundred 8 tens 13 ones becomes 1 hundred 9 tens 3 ones. When I solve the problem another way, it is just like showing the 3 parts before renaming. 1 hundred 8 tens 13 ones = $100 + 80 + 13$. I can add the parts in any order and get the same total!

G2-M4-Lesson 31

Solve the following word problems by drawing a tape diagram. Then, use any strategy that you've learned to solve.

Sandra has 46 fewer coins than Martha. Sandra has 57 coins.

a. How many coins does Martha have?

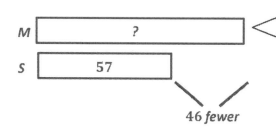

> I use the RDW process to solve. A tape diagram helps me see the parts I know. I know that Sandra has 46 fewer coins than Martha, so that means Martha has more coins, 46 more. I add to find the number of coins Martha has.

> I use a number bond and the make ten strategy to solve!

$57 + 3 = 60$
$60 + 43 = 103$

Martha has 103 coins.

b. How many coins do Sandra and Martha have together?

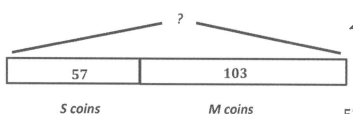

S coins   M coins

> From Part (a), I know that Martha has 103 coins. I add them to Sandra's 57 coins to get 160 coins all together.

$57 + 103 = ?$
$57 + 100 + 3 = ?$
$60 + 100 = 160$

Sandra and Martha have 160 coins together.

> I break 103 into $100 + 3$ and then add the 3 to 57 to make the friendly number 60. Now, this problem is easy: $60 + 100 = 160$.

Homework Helpers

Grade 2
Module 5

G2-M5-Lesson 1

1. Complete each *more* or *less* statement.

   a. 10 less than 175 is <u>165</u>.

   b. 100 more than 308 is <u>408</u>.

   c. <u>788</u> is 100 less than 888.

   d. 607 is <u>10 more</u> than 597.

   > I can use place value language to explain the change. 10 more and 100 more is the same as adding. 10 less and 100 less is the same as subtracting.

2. Complete each regular number pattern.

   a. 565, 575, <u>585, 595, 605</u>, 615

   b. 624, <u>524, 424, 324, 224</u>, 124, 24

   c. <u>886, 876, 866</u>, 856, 846, 836

   > I study the numbers and look for the more or less pattern. I know 24 is 100 less than 124, so $24 + 100 = 124$. Then, $124 + 100 = 224$, and so on.

   > I know 846 is 10 less than 856. $856 - 10 = 846$. It's just like taking away a tens disk on the place value chart.

3. Complete each statement.

   a. $609 \xrightarrow{-10} \underline{599} \xrightarrow{-100} 499 \xrightarrow{+10} \underline{509} \xrightarrow{+10} 519$

   b. $517 \xrightarrow{-10} \underline{507} \xrightarrow{-10} \underline{497} \xrightarrow{+100} \underline{597} \xrightarrow{+10} \underline{607} \xrightarrow{+100} \underline{707}$

   > I remember the arrow way from Module 4. The arrow way can show a change in the ones, tens, or hundreds place, and it shows whether it's more or less. So, $517 - 10 = 507$. That's a change in the tens place!

4. Solve using the arrow way.

   $\underline{220} + 515 = 735$

   $515 \xrightarrow{+100} 615 \xrightarrow{+100} 715 \xrightarrow{+10} 725 \xrightarrow{+10} 735$

   > I start with the part, 515, and add hundreds first until I get to 715. Then, I add tens until I get to 735. $100 + 100 + 10 + 10 = 220$.

G2-M5-Lesson 2

1. Solve each addition problem using place value strategies. Use the arrow way or mental math, and record your answers. You may use scrap paper if you like.

    a. $400 + 374 = \underline{774}$

    > To solve $400 + 374$, I just add like units!
    > 4 hundreds + 3 hundreds = 7 hundreds. The ones and tens digits stay the same, so the total is 774.

    b. $\underline{126} + 600 = 726$

    $$600 \xrightarrow{+100} 700 \xrightarrow{+26} 726$$

    > I use the arrow way to solve _____ + 600 = 726.
    > I begin at 600 and add 1 hundred to get to 700.
    > Then, I add on 26. $100 + 26 = 126$.

2. Solve each subtraction problem using place value strategies. Use the arrow way or mental math, and record your answers. You may use scrap paper if you like.

    a. $431 - \underline{300} = 131$

    > The number in the hundreds place got smaller by 3. The other part must be 300 because 4 hundreds minus 3 hundreds equals 1 hundred. The other digits stay the same.

    b. $\underline{862} - 200 = 662$

    $$662 \xrightarrow{+200} 862$$

    > I know the 2 parts, but I don't know the whole. I use the arrow way and think of addition to solve: $662 + 200 = 862$.

3. Fill in the blanks to make true number sentences. Use place value strategies, number bonds, or the arrow way to solve.

    a. 400 less than 842 is $\underline{442}$.

    $$842 - 400$$

    $$\bigwedge$$

    $$800 \qquad 42$$

    $800 - 400 = 400$
    $400 + 42 = 442$

    > I draw a number bond to break apart 842. I subtract 400 from 800, which is 400. Then I add 400 to the other part, so $400 + 42 = 442$.

    b. $\underline{700}$ less than 962 is 262.

    c. 300 *more* than 545 is 845.

    > 300 *more* than 545 is the same as $545 + 300$. $500 + 300 = 800$. The ones and tens stay the same.

2   **Lesson 2:**   Add and subtract multiples of 100, including counting on to subtract.

©2015 Great Minds. eureka-math.org
G2-M1-HWH-1.3.0-07.2015

G2-M5-Lesson 3

1. Solve the set of problems using the arrow way.

   $440 + 300 = \underline{740}$

   $440 \xrightarrow{+300} 740$

   > 300 more than 440 is 740. I just add like units, 4 hundreds plus 3 hundreds is 7 hundreds. The tens and ones stay the same.

   $440 + 360 = \underline{800}$

   $440 \xrightarrow{+300} 740 \xrightarrow{+60} 800$

   > To add 360, I add in chunks—hundreds first and then tens. 4 tens + 6 tens = 10 tens, or the next hundred!

   $440 + 380 = \underline{820}$

   $440 \xrightarrow{+300} 740 \xrightarrow{+60} 800 \xrightarrow{+20} 820$

   > The second problem helps me solve this one. 380 is just 20 more than 360. I use the arrow way to add 20. Now, the total is 820.

2. Solve using the arrow way or mental math. Use scrap paper if needed.

   $430 + 290 = \underline{\quad 720 \quad}$ $660 + 180 = \underline{\quad 840 \quad}$ $370 + 270 = \underline{\quad 640 \quad}$

   420   10

   $660 \xrightarrow{+100} 760 \xrightarrow{+40} 800 \xrightarrow{+40} 840$

   > I made a number bond on scrap paper. 290 is close to the next hundred, it just needs 10 more. I broke apart 430 into 420 and 10. I add 10 to 290 and now can solve 420 + 300 in my head.

   > I can solve in my head! 3 hundreds plus 2 hundreds is 5 hundreds. I know 7 tens plus 7 tens is 14 tens, or 140. I can think: 500 + 140 = 640.

   > This is similar to adding 66 and 27, except the units are tens! 6 tens and 7 tens is 13 tens. 60 tens and 20 tens is 80 tens. 13 tens + 80 tens = 93 tens.

   > The first problem can help me solve this one. I notice that 67 tens is 1 more ten than 66 tens. 28 tens is 1 more ten than 27 tens. That means the answer must be 2 more tens than 93 tens!

3. Solve.

   66 tens + 27 tens = __93__ tens   67 tens + 28 tens = __95__ tens

   What is the value of 85 tens? __850__

G2-M5-Lesson 4

1. Solve using the arrow way.

    $760 - 400 = \underline{360}$

    > I just subtract like units, 7 hundreds minus 4 hundreds is 3 hundreds. The tens and ones stay the same.

    $760 \xrightarrow{-400} 360$

    $760 - 460 = \underline{300}$

    > To subtract 460, I first take away the hundreds and then tens to make it easier!

    $760 \xrightarrow{-400} 360 \xrightarrow{-60} 300$

    $760 - 480 = \underline{280}$

    > The other problems help me solve this one. First, I subtract 400 and then 60 to get to the closest hundred, and now I subtract 20 more. So, I take away 480 in all, one chunk at a time.

    $760 \xrightarrow{-400} 360 \xrightarrow{-60} 300 \xrightarrow{-20} 280$

2. Solve using the arrow way or mental math. Use scrap paper if needed.

    $640 - 240 = \underline{400}$ $640 - 250 = \underline{390}$ $640 - 290 = \underline{350}$

    $640 \xrightarrow{-200} 440 \xrightarrow{-40} 400$ $640 \xrightarrow{-200} 440 \xrightarrow{-40} 400 \xrightarrow{-50} 350$

    > I subtract in two steps. First, I take away the hundreds and then the tens. 640 minus 200 is 440. 440 minus 40 is 400.

    > I can use the last problem to help me. In my head, I subtract 10 more from 400 since 250 is just 10 more than 240.

    > I subtract 290 in chunks: 200, then 40, and then 50. In the last step, I subtract 50 to get to 350.

Lesson 4:   Subtract multiples of 100 and some tens within 1,000.

EUREKA MATH™

I know that 88 tens minus 20 tens is 68 tens. Then, 68 tens minus 8 tens is 60 tens. Now, I just take away another ten. So, I have 59 tens.

I could also think of it like this: 88 tens minus 28 tens is 60 tens. Since 29 tens is 1 more than 28 tens, the answer must be 1 less than 60 tens.

I subtract a total of 28 tens, one chunk at a time. 84 tens minus 20 tens is 64 tens. Now, I take away 4 tens, so I have 60 tens and then 4 more tens, which makes 56 tens.

3. Solve.

88 tens − 29 tens = __59 tens__   84 tens − 28 tens = __56 tens__

What is the value of 56 tens? __560__

©2015 Great Minds. eureka-math.org
G2-M1-HWH-1.3.0-07.2015

G2-M5-Lesson 5

1. Solve.

> When I have a zero in the ones place, I can think of the number as "some tens"!

43 tens = __430__

24 tens + 19 tens = __43__ tens   25 tens + 29 tens = __54__ tens

> This is similar to 24 + 19 except I am adding tens instead of ones! 19 is just 1 away from 20, so I add 24 tens + 20 tens = 44 tens. Then, I subtract 1 ten and get 43 tens.

> I can use the same idea as the last problem! 25 tens + 30 tens = 55 tens. Since there are only 29 tens, I subtract 1 ten and get 54 tens.

2. Add by drawing a number bond to make a hundred. Write the simplified equation and solve.

a.   330 + 180

310   20

__310 + 200__ = __510__

> I can use a number bond to add when one number is close to the next hundred. 180 is close to 200. I need 20 more. I can get it from the 330. I break apart 330 into 310 and 20. Now my problem is 310 + 200, which is easier to solve. I can just count on 2 hundreds.

b.   153 + 499

152   1

__152 + 500__ = __652__

> 499 is only 1 away from 500. I can decompose 153 into 152 and 1. Then, I add the 1 to 499 to get 500. My new addition problem is 152 + 500 = 652.

c.   695 + 178

5   173

__700 + 173__ = __873__

> 695 is closer to the next hundred than 178. I break apart 178 into 5 and 173. I give 5 to 695, so 700 + 173 = 873.

EUREKA
MATH

©2015 Great Minds. eureka-math.org
G2-M1-HWH-1.3.0-07.2015

G2-M5-Lesson 6

1. Draw and label a tape diagram to show how to simplify the problem. Write the new equation, and then subtract.

   a. $570 - 380 = \underline{\quad 590 - 400 \quad} = \underline{\quad 190 \quad}$

+20	570

+20	380

   > It's easier to take away hundreds! If I add the same amount, 20, to each number, I have a simpler problem. This is called compensation! Now, I can easily subtract 400 from 590.

   b. $450 - 170 = \underline{\quad 480 - 200 \quad} = \underline{\quad 280 \quad}$

+30	450

+30	170

   > I see that 170 is close to 200. I add 30 to each number, so the difference stays the same. My new problem is $480 - 200$.

2. Draw and label a tape diagram to show how to simplify the problem. Write a new equation, and then subtract. Check your work using addition.

   a. $483 - 299 = \underline{\quad 484 - 300 \quad} = \underline{\quad 184 \quad}$

+1	483

+1	299

   Check:

   $184 + 300 = 484$

   > I check my work by adding the 2 parts. The sum should be 484.

   > I only need to add 1 to each number to make this problem easier! If I add 1 to both numbers, I can subtract only hundreds, instead of hundreds, tens, and ones!

   > This is much easier than the vertical form because I don't have to rename! I just add 2 to both numbers, and then I can solve in my head!

   b. $776 - 598 = \underline{\quad 778 - 600 \quad} = \underline{\quad 178 \quad}$

+2	776

+2	598

   Check:

   $178 + 600 = 778$

EUREKA MATH™   **Lesson 6:**   Use the associative property to subtract from three-digit numbers and verify solutions with addition.   7

©2015 Great Minds. eureka-math.org
G2-M1-HWH-1.3.0-07.2015

G2-M5-Lesson 7

1. Solve each problem with a written strategy such as a tape diagram, a number bond, the arrow way, the vertical form, or chips on a place value chart.

$780 - 390 = \underline{390}$

+ 10	780
+ 10	390

390 is only 10 away from 400. I draw a tape diagram to show how I add 10 to both numbers so the difference stays the same. My new problem is $790 - 400 = 390$.

$\underline{331} + 600 = 931$

$$600 \xrightarrow{+300} 900 \xrightarrow{+31} 931$$

I use the arrow way to add in chunks. First, I add 3 hundreds to get to 900. Then, I add 31 more to get to 931. $300 + 31 = 331$

$\underline{280} = 560 - 280$

+ 20	560
+ 20	280

I use compensation and add 20 to both numbers. So, my easier problem is $580 - 300 = 280$. I don't have to unbundle a hundred!

2. Use the arrow way to complete the number sentence.

$820 - 340 = \underline{480}$

$$820 \xrightarrow{-300} 520 \xrightarrow{-20} 500 \xrightarrow{-20} 480$$

I use the arrow way to subtract hundreds and then tens. When I get to 520, I subtract 20 to get to the hundred and then 20 more to get to 480.

3. Solve $447 + 398$ using two different strategies.

a.	b.
$447 + 398 = \underline{845}$	$447 + 398 = \underline{845}$
$447 \xrightarrow{+300} 747 \xrightarrow{+3} 750 \xrightarrow{+50} 800 \xrightarrow{+40} 840 \xrightarrow{+5} 845$	445 2 $445 + 400 = 845$

c. Explain which strategy is easier to use when solving and why.

It is much easier for me to solve with a number bond because 398 is only 2 away from the next

hundred. The arrow way takes a long time, and I have to make sure I don't miss any parts of

the number 398. The number bond has a lot fewer steps!

EUREKA MATH

©2015 Great Minds. eureka-math.org
G2-M1-HWH-1.3.0-07.2015

G2-M5-Lesson 8

1. Solve the following problems using your place value chart, place value disks, and vertical form. Bundle a ten or hundred when necessary.

$516 + 224$

```
    5  1  6
  + 2  2  4
  ─────────
```

> I write the problem in vertical form and model both addends with my place value disks.

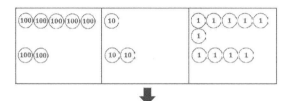

```
    5  1  6
  + 2  2  4
  ─────────
         1
         0
```

> 6 ones plus 4 ones is 10 ones, or 1 ten 0 ones. I record this in vertical form on the line below the tens place by first showing the new unit of ten using new groups below. Then, I write 0 below the ones place.

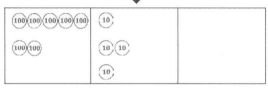

```
    5  1  6
  + 2  2  4
  ─────────
         1
    7  4  0
```

> Next, I add the tens and then the hundreds. 1 ten plus 2 tens plus 1 more ten is 4 tens. 5 hundreds plus 2 hundreds is 7 hundreds.
>
> $516 + 224 = 740$

2. Solve.

    a. $600 + 180 = \underline{780}$

    > Easy! $600 + 100 = 700$. Then I add on 80, so 780.

    b. $620 + 180 = \underline{800}$
        $\wedge$
       600 20

    > I can break 620 into 600 and 20 to make an easier problem to solve. When I add the 20 to 180 I get 200, and $600 + 200 = 800$, so $620 + 180 = 800$.

    c. $680 + 220 = \underline{900}$

    > $600 + 200 = 800$
    > $80 + 20 = 100$
    > $800 + 100 = 900$

       800 100

    d. $680 + 230 = \underline{910}$

    > Part (c) helps me solve this one. The first addend, 680, is the same. 230 is just 10 more than 220. That means the answer must be 10 more than 900, or 910.

G2-M5-Lesson 9

1. Solve the following problems using your place value chart, place value disks, and vertical form. Bundle a ten or hundred when necessary.

$346 + 278$

> I show each step with the place value disks in the vertical form. When I make a new unit, I show it with new groups below.

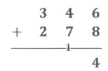

> When I add the ones, I have 14 ones, or 1 ten 4 ones. I change 10 ones for 1 ten.

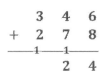

> Next, I add 4 tens plus 7 tens plus 1 more ten. That's 12 tens, or 1 hundred 2 tens. I change 10 tens for 1 hundred.

> Now I have 6 hundreds 2 tens 4 ones. $346 + 278 = 624$

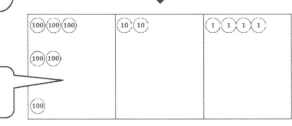

2. Solve.

a. $478 + 303 = \underline{781}$

$\wedge$
2   301

> 478 is close to 480; it only needs 2 more. I can take 2 from 303 by breaking 303 into 2 and 301 to make an easier problem. $480 + 301 = 781$, so $478 + 303 = 781$.

b. $478 + 323 = \underline{801}$

> Part (a) helps me solve this problem. 323 is just 20 more than 303, so the answer must be 20 more than 781. I count on 2 tens from 781. $781, 791, 801$.

©2015 Great Minds. eureka-math.org
G2-M1-HWH-1.3.0-07.2015

G2-M5-Lesson 10

Solve using vertical form, and draw chips on the place value chart. Bundle as needed.

$306 + 596 =$ __902__

I show each step I make with chips vertically using new groups below.

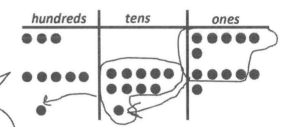

```
    3   0   6
+   5   9   6
    1   1
    9   0   2
```

I draw chips to show each addend. I draw 3 chips in the hundreds place, 0 chips in the tens place, and 6 chips in the ones place to represent 306. Since I am adding, I also draw chips to show 596.

The place value chart and the vertical form both show the same thing: there are 9 hundreds 0 tens 2 ones. That's 902.

6 ones plus 6 ones is 12 ones, or 1 ten 2 ones. I bundle 10 ones to make 1 ten. Now I add the tens. 9 tens plus the new ten is 10 tens. I can bundle again! 10 tens makes 1 hundred.

Lesson 10: Use math drawings to represent additions with up to two compositions and relate drawings to the addition algorithm.

11

G2-M5-Lesson 11

Solve using vertical form, and draw chips on the place value chart. Bundle as needed.

$276 + 324 =$ __600__

I draw chips to represent each addend.

```
    2   7   6
+   3   2   4
    1   1
    6   0   0
```

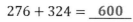

hundreds	tens	ones

My chip model matches the vertical form. I bundled twice, and I show the new units with new groups below.

Renaming the tens is just like renaming the ones. I have to look for 10 of a unit to make the next higher value unit. So, 10 ones make 1 ten, and 10 tens make 1 hundred!

12   Lesson 11:   Use math drawings to represent additions with up to two compositions
                                 and relate drawings to the addition algorithm.

                    ©2015 Great Minds. eureka-math.org
                    G2-M1-HWH-1.3.0-07.2015

EUREKA
MATH

G2-M5-Lesson 12

1. Solve $246 + 490$ using two different strategies.

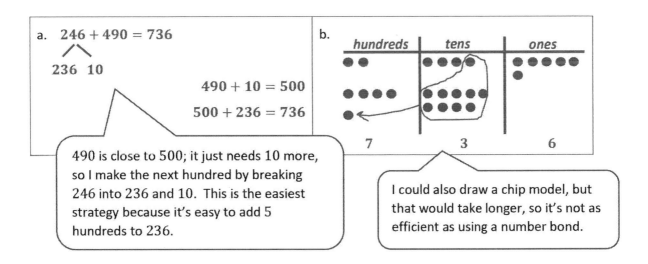

a. $246 + 490 = 736$

   236 10

   $490 + 10 = 500$

   $500 + 236 = 736$

   490 is close to 500; it just needs 10 more, so I make the next hundred by breaking 246 into 236 and 10. This is the easiest strategy because it's easy to add 5 hundreds to 236.

b.

   | hundreds | tens | ones |

   7   3   6

   I could also draw a chip model, but that would take longer, so it's not as efficient as using a number bond.

2. Choose the best strategy and solve. Explain why you chose that strategy.

   a. $499 + 367 = \underline{866}$

      1   366

      The best strategy is to make the next hundred to make an easier problem to solve. 499 needs just 1 more to be 500. Then, it's easy to add what's left, 366. $500 + 366 = 866$, so $499 + 367 = 866$. That's why it's important to always look for relationships between the numbers.

   b. $534 + 110 = \underline{644}$

      I can solve this one mentally by adding like units. $500 + 100 = 600$, and $34 + 10 = 44$, so $600 + 44 = 644$.

   c. $695 + 248 = \underline{943}$

      5   243

      At first, I thought I needed to use the chip model and vertical form because I can see I need to rename twice. But then I looked more carefully! I see that I can make the next hundred, so I break apart 248. $695 + 5 = 700$, and $700 + 243 = 943$, so $695 + 248 = 943$.

G2-M5-Lesson 13

> I can use $180 - 30$ to help me solve $180 - 29$. Since the difference in the first problem is 150, the difference in the second problem must be 1 more than 150 because I am subtracting 1 less.

1. Solve using mental math.

$8 - 3 = \underline{\ 5\ }$ $80 - 30 = \underline{\ 50\ }$ $180 - 30 = \underline{\ 150\ }$ $180 - 29 = \underline{\ 151\ }$

2. Solve using mental math or vertical form with place value disks. Check your work using addition.

   a. $223 - 121 = \underline{\ 102\ }$

   > I can use mental math to solve because there's no renaming. I just subtract like units. $200 - 100 = 100$, $20 - 20 = 0$, and $3 - 1 = 2$. $100 + 2 = 102$, so $223 - 121 = 102$. I can check my work by adding: $102 + 121 = 223$.

   b. $378 - 119 = \underline{\ 259\ }$

   > I can solve this one mentally, too, using compensation. If I add 1 to each number, I make a problem that's easier to solve, $379 - 120$. There's no renaming, so I just subtract like units. The answer is 259.

+1	378

+1	119

   > I know that part plus part equals whole, so if I'm right, $259 + 119$ must equal 378. When I check my work, I see that I'm right!

   ```
       2  5  9
    +  1  1  9
   ----1-------
       3  7  8
   ```

3. Complete the number sentence modeled by place value disks.

   > The model shows the whole, 342. 2 hundreds 2 tens 5 ones are crossed off. That's 225. That means the number sentence is $342 - 225 = 117$. I can check to see if I'm right by adding 117 and 225.

   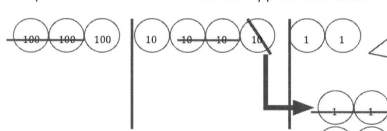

   $\underline{342} - \underline{225} = 117$

   ```
       1  1  7
    +  2  2  5
   ----1-------
       3  4  2
   ```

Lesson 13:   Relate manipulative representations to the subtraction algorithm, and
                            use addition to explain why the subtraction method works.

©2015 Great Minds. eureka-math.org
G2-M1-HWH-1.3.0-07.2015

G2-M5-Lesson 14

1. Solve by drawing place value disks on a chart. Then, use addition to check your work.

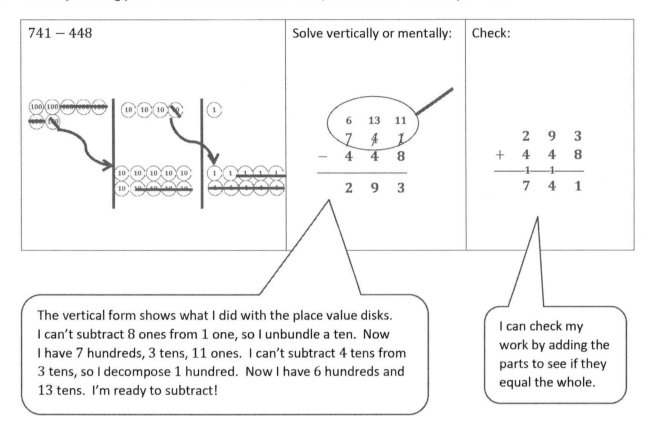

The vertical form shows what I did with the place value disks. I can't subtract 8 ones from 1 one, so I unbundle a ten. Now I have 7 hundreds, 3 tens, 11 ones. I can't subtract 4 tens from 3 tens, so I decompose 1 hundred. Now I have 6 hundreds and 13 tens. I'm ready to subtract!

I can check my work by adding the parts to see if they equal the whole.

2. If $584 - 147 = 437$, then $437 + 147 = 584$. Explain why this statement is true using numbers, pictures, or words.

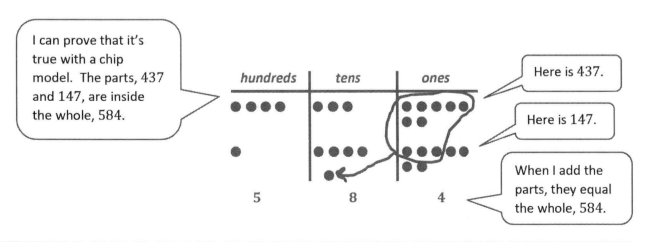

I can prove that it's true with a chip model. The parts, 437 and 147, are inside the whole, 584.

Here is 437.

Here is 147.

When I add the parts, they equal the whole, 584.

EUREKA MATH™

Lesson 14: Use math drawings to represent subtraction with up to two decompositions, relate drawings to the algorithm, and use addition to explain why the subtraction method works.

©2015 Great Minds. eureka-math.org
G2-M1-HWH-1.3.0-07.2015

15

G2-M5-Lesson 15

1. Solve by drawing chips on the place value chart. Then, use addition to check your work.

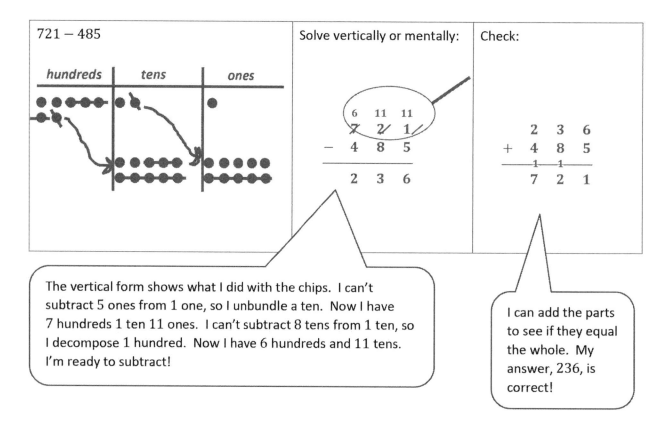

721 − 485

| hundreds | tens | ones |

Solve vertically or mentally:

Check:

$$\begin{array}{r} {\scriptstyle 6\ \ 11\ \ 11} \\ 7\ \ 2\!\!\!/\ \ 1\!\!\!/ \\ -\ 4\ \ 8\ \ 5 \\ \hline 2\ \ 3\ \ 6 \end{array}$$

$$\begin{array}{r} 2\ \ 3\ \ 6 \\ +\ 4\ \ 8\ \ 5 \\ \hline 7\ \ 2\ \ 1 \end{array}$$

The vertical form shows what I did with the chips. I can't subtract 5 ones from 1 one, so I unbundle a ten. Now I have 7 hundreds 1 ten 11 ones. I can't subtract 8 tens from 1 ten, so I decompose 1 hundred. Now I have 6 hundreds and 11 tens. I'm ready to subtract!

I can add the parts to see if they equal the whole. My answer, 236, is correct!

2. Complete the *if...then* statement. Draw a number bond to represent the related facts.

If $631 - \underline{\ 358\ } = 273$, then $\underline{\ 358\ } + 273 = 631$.

The number bond shows the part–whole relationship.

I know that whole − part = part. 631 is the whole because it's the largest number. 273 is the part I know, so I can subtract to find the other part: $631 - 273 = 358$. That also means that $358 + 273 = 631$ because part + part = whole.

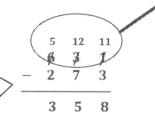

$$\begin{array}{r} {\scriptstyle 5\ \ 12\ \ 11} \\ 6\ \ 3\ \ 1 \\ -\ 2\ \ 7\ \ 3 \\ \hline 3\ \ 5\ \ 8 \end{array}$$

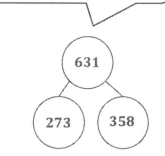

Lesson 15:   Use math drawings to represent subtraction with up to two
                        decompositions, relate drawings to the algorithm, and use addition to
                        explain why the subtraction method works.

©2015 Great Minds. eureka-math.org
G2-M1-HWH-1.3.0-07.2015

EUREKA
MATH

G2-M5-Lesson 16

1. Solve vertically or using mental math. Draw chips on the place value chart and unbundle if needed.

   a. $408 - 261 = \underline{147}$

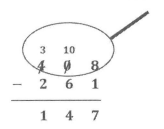
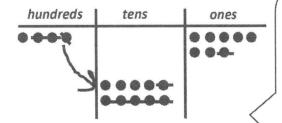

> The vertical form shows what I did with the chips. I have enough ones to subtract in the ones place, but I need to unbundle 1 hundred to have enough tens in the tens place. Now I'm ready to subtract!

   b. $700 - 568 = \underline{132}$

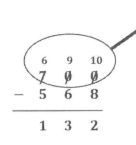
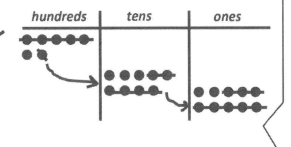

> I see that both the tens and the ones are going to need more. I can unbundle a hundred in one step. 1 hundred is equal to 9 tens 10 ones. Now I have 6 hundreds 9 tens 10 ones. I show this with my chips and in the vertical form. Now, I am ready to subtract.

2. Emily said that $400 - 247$ is the same as $399 - 246$. Write an explanation using pictures, numbers, or words to prove Emily is correct.

> I can use compensation. I notice that 400 is just 1 more than 399, and 247 is just 1 more than 246. So, the difference for each problem must be the same!

> I can explain two different ways!

> I can use the arrow way to show that the difference is the same. $400 - 247 = 153$, and $399 - 246 = 153$.

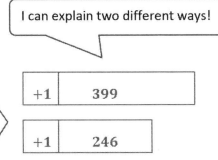

$$400 \xrightarrow{-200} 200 \xrightarrow{-40} 160 \xrightarrow{-7} 153$$

$$399 \xrightarrow{-200} 199 \xrightarrow{-40} 159 \xrightarrow{-6} 153$$

G2-M5-Lesson 17

Solve vertically or using mental math. Draw chips on the place value chart and unbundle if needed.

a. $500 - 231 =$ __269__

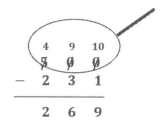

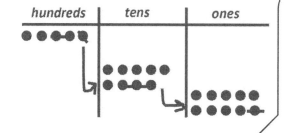

> I see that both the tens and the ones are going to need more. I can unbundle a hundred in one step. 1 hundred is equal to 9 tens 10 ones. Now I have 4 hundreds 9 tens 10 ones. I show this with my chips and in the vertical form. I am ready to subtract.

b. $902 - 306 =$ __596__

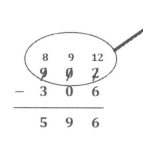

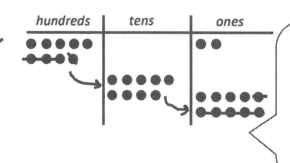

> I change 1 hundred for 9 tens 10 ones. Now I have 8 hundreds 9 tens 12 ones. I show my work with the chips and in the vertical form. I am ready to subtract.

> I can check my work using addition.
> $596 + 306 = 902$

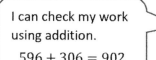

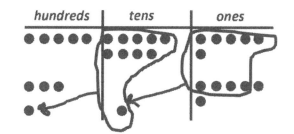

Lesson 17:   Subtract from multiples of 100 and from numbers with zero in the tens place.

EUREKA
MATH™

G2-M5-Lesson 18

1. Use the arrow way and counting on to solve.

$$300 - 164 = 136 \qquad 164 \xrightarrow{+6} 170 \xrightarrow{+30} 200 \xrightarrow{+100} 300$$

> The arrow way is efficient. I add ones, tens, and hundreds to get to benchmark, or friendly, numbers. That makes counting on easy!

> I added $6 + 30 + 100$. That equals 136. So $300 - 164 = 136$.

2. Choose a strategy to solve, and explain why you chose that strategy.

$$500 - 280 = 220$$

+20	500

+20	280

> Compensation works best for this problem because I notice 280 is close to 300. It's easy to subtract 300, so I add 20 to each number. That makes a problem that's easier to solve, $520 - 300 = 220$. So $500 - 280 = 220$.

3. Explain why $400 - 173$ is the same as $399 - 172$.

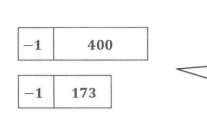

−1	400

−1	173

> I can explain by using compensation like I did for Problem 2, except this time I'll subtract. When I subtract 1 from each number in $400 - 173$, I see that the expression becomes $399 - 172$!

$$400 - 173 = 399 - 172$$

EUREKA MATH   **Lesson 18:**   Apply and explain alternate methods for subtracting from multiples of 100 and from numbers with zero in the tens place.   **19**

©2015 Great Minds. eureka-math.org
G2-M1-HWH-1.3.0-07.2015

G2-M5-Lesson 19

Solve and explain why you chose that strategy.

a. $580 + 230 = \underline{\ 810\ }$
      $\wedge$

> I notice I can make the next hundred because 580 is close to 600. I break apart 230 into 20 and 210. 600 more than 210 is easy, 810.

b. $310 + \underline{\ 333\ } = 643$

      $643 - 310 = 333$

> To find a missing addend, I can subtract. If I subtract one part from the whole, the answer is the missing part. I rewrite the problem as $643 - 310$. There's no renaming so I just subtract like units, hundreds from hundreds, tens from tens, and ones from ones.

c. $900 - 327 = \underline{\ 573\ }$

      $327 \xrightarrow{+3} 330 \xrightarrow{+70} 400 \xrightarrow{+500} 900$

> The arrow way is easy because I just need to reach a benchmark number, and then I can skip-count quickly. $327 + 3$ gets me to 330. 330 needs 70 to get to 400. Now I just add 500 to reach 900. Altogether, I added 573, so $900 - 327 = 573$.

d. $802 - 698 = \underline{\ 104\ }$

+2	802
+2	698

> I can use compensation. I notice that 698 is very close to 700, which is an easy number to subtract. I add 2 to 698 to get 700. What I do to one number I must do to the other number, so I add 2 to 802. Now I have an easier problem to solve, $804 - 700$. Easy! The answer is 104.

Lesson 19:   Choose and explain solution strategies and record with a written addition or subtraction method.

EUREKA MATH

G2-M5-Lesson 20

1. Solve each problem using two different strategies.

$295 + \underline{\ 239\ } = 534$

a. First Strategy	b. Second Strategy

a.   **First Strategy**

$$295 \xrightarrow{+5} 300 \xrightarrow{+200} 500 \xrightarrow{+34} 534$$

> I can solve by counting on. I use the arrow way to show what I add to 295 to reach 534.
>
> $200 + 34 + 5 = 239$

b.   **Second Strategy**

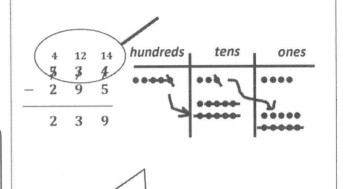

> I can also solve by using a chip model, and I show my work in vertical form.

2. Circle a strategy to solve and explain why you chose that strategy.

$843 - 698 = \underline{\ 145\ }$ *Number bond or* (arrow way)

$$698 \xrightarrow{+2} 700 \xrightarrow{+100} 800 \xrightarrow{+43} 843$$

> I chose the arrow way because I see that 698 is close to 700. I just add 2. From there, I can add 100 to reach 800. Then I just add 43 more to reach 843. $100 + 43 + 2 = 145$

EUREKA MATH   Lesson 20:   Choose and explain solution strategies and record with a written addition or subtraction method.   21

©2015 Great Minds. eureka-math.org
G2-M1-HWH-1.3.0-07.2015

Homework Helpers

Grade 2
Module 6

G2-M6-Lesson 1

> $2 + 2 + 2 = 6$
> I can think $2 + 2 = 4$ and $4 + 2 = 6$.

> $3 \times 2 = 6$
> I can think 3 groups of 2 equals 6.

Repeated addition in Grade 2 ...   leads to multiplication in Grade 3.

> By putting the apples into groups of 2,
> I create 5 equal groups of two apples.

1. Circle groups of two apples.

There are ___5___ groups of two apples.

> I can make different equal
> groups out of the same total.

2. Redraw the 12 oranges into 4 equal groups.

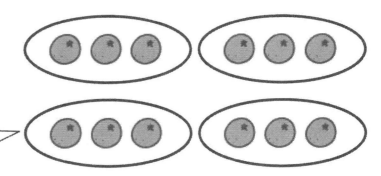

> I can group 12 oranges into 4
> groups of 3 or 3 groups of 4.

4 groups of ___3___ oranges

3. Redraw the 12 oranges into 3 equal groups.

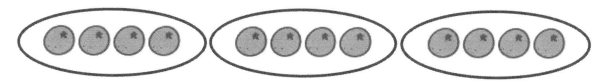

3 groups of __4__ oranges

I can turn unequal groups into equal groups.

4. Redraw the flowers to make each of the 3 groups have an equal number.

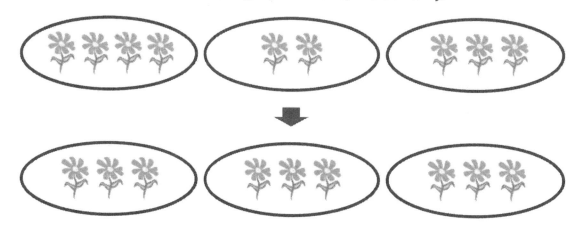

3 groups of __3__ flowers = __9__ flowers.

Lesson 1:   Use manipulatives to create equal groups.

EUREKA
MATH™

G2-M6-Lesson 2

1. Write a repeated addition equation to show the number of objects in each group. Then, find the total.

$$\underline{\ 2\ } + \underline{\ 2\ } + \underline{\ 2\ } = \underline{\ 6\ }$$

3 groups of __2__ = __6__

> There are 2 pencils in each group, so the repeated addition sentence is $2 + 2 + 2 = 6$. We can say 3 groups of 2 equals 6.

2. Draw 1 more group of three. Then, write a repeated addition equation to match.

$$\underline{\ 3\ } + \underline{\ 3\ } + \underline{\ 3\ } + \underline{\ 3\ } = \underline{\ 12\ }$$

__4__ groups of 3 = __12__

> When I draw another group of 3 boxes, I have to add another 3 to the repeated addition sentence because now there are 4 groups of 3.

©2015 Great Minds. eureka-math.org
G2-M1-HWH-1.3.0-07.2015

G2-M6-Lesson 3

1. Write a repeated addition equation to match the picture. Then, group the addends into pairs to show a more efficient way to add.

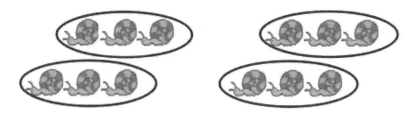

$$\underline{\;3\;} + \underline{\;3\;} + \underline{\;3\;} + \underline{\;3\;} = \underline{\;12\;}$$

$$\backslash \quad / \qquad \backslash \quad /$$

$$\underline{\;6\;} \quad + \quad \underline{\;6\;} = \underline{\;12\;}$$

4 groups of _3_ = 2 groups of _6_

> I can group addends into pairs and use doubles to add quickly. I know $3 + 3 = 6$, and since there are two sixes, I can add $6 + 6$ to get 12.

2.

$$\underline{\;3\;} + \underline{\;3\;} + \underline{\;3\;} + \underline{\;3\;} + \underline{\;3\;} = \underline{\;15\;}$$

$$\underline{\;6\;} + \underline{\;6\;} + 3 = \underline{\;15\;}$$

> If there is an extra addend, I can still use doubles and then just add on that extra amount.

$$\underline{\;12\;} + 3 = \underline{\;15\;}$$

Lesson 3:   Use math drawings to represent equal groups, and relate to repeated addition.

EUREKA
MATH

G2-M6-Lesson 4

1. Write a repeated addition equation to find the total of each tape diagram.

> This tape diagram drawing helps me see that there are 4 groups with 2 cups in each group.

__2__ + __2__ + __2__ + __2__ = __8__

4 groups of 2 = __8__

> The boxes represent the groups.

> To find the total, I add 4 groups of 2.
> $2 + 2 + 2 + 2 = 8$

2. Draw a tape diagram to find the total.

    5 groups of 2

| 2 | 2 | 2 | 2 | 2 |

$2 + 2 + 2 + 2 + 2 = 10$

> The boxes represent the groups. There are 5 groups, so I draw 5 boxes.

> There are 2 in each group. Instead of drawing a picture, I can just write the number 2 in each box.

> To find the total, I add 5 groups of 2.
> $2 + 2 + 2 + 2 + 2 = 10$

G2-M6-Lesson 5

1. Circle groups of two. Redraw the groups of two as rows and then as columns.

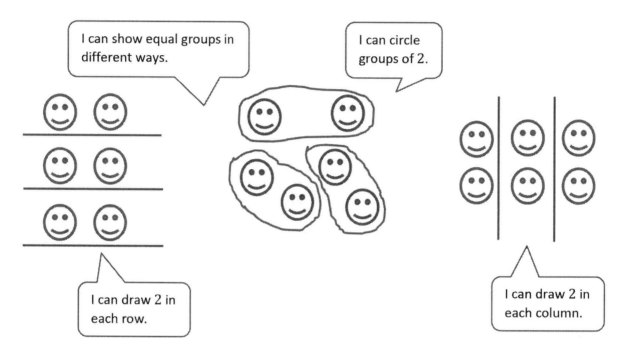

2. Count the objects in the array from left to right by rows and top to bottom by columns. As you count, circle the rows and then the columns.

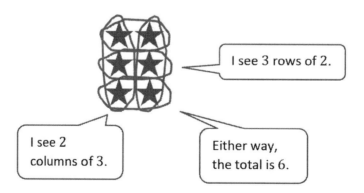

Lesson 5:   Compose arrays from rows and columns, and count to find the total using objects.

EUREKA MATH

©2015 Great Minds. eureka-math.org
G2-M1-HWH-1.3.0-07.2015

G2-M6-Lesson 6

Use the array of shaded triangles to answer the questions below.

a.   __3__ rows of __4__ = 12

b.   __4__ columns of __3__ = 12

c.   __4__ + __4__ + __4__ = __12__

d.   Add 1 more row. How many triangles are there now? __16__

> When another row or column is added so is another group, or unit. I just think $12 + 4 = 16$.

e.   Remove 1 column from the new array you made. How many triangles are there now? __12__

> When a row or column is removed, I take away one group, or unit. I know 4 less than 16 is 12.

EUREKA MATH™

Lesson 6: Decompose arrays into rows and columns, and relate to repeated addition.

©2015 Great Minds. eureka-math.org
G2-M1-HWH-1.3.0-07.2015

7

G2-M6-Lesson 7

1. Draw an array with X's that has 3 columns of 4. Draw vertical lines to separate the columns. Fill in the blanks.

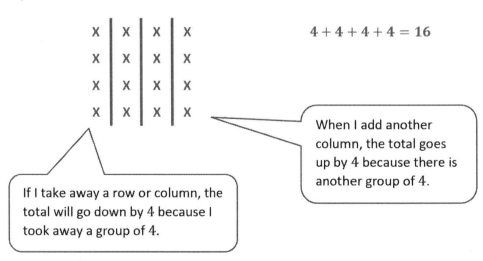

X │ X │ X
X │ X │ X
X │ X │ X
X │ X │ X

__4__ + __4__ + __4__ = __12__

3 columns of 4 = __12__

3 rows of 4 = __12__

In this problem, the column is the group, but I can imagine turning the array on its side and seeing 3 rows of 4.

3 columns of 4 and 3 rows of 4 is the same array. It's just a different way of looking at the same amount!

2. Draw an array of X's with 1 more column of 4 than the array shown above. Write a repeated addition equation to find the total number of X's.

X │ X │ X │ X
X │ X │ X │ X
X │ X │ X │ X
X │ X │ X │ X

$4 + 4 + 4 + 4 = 16$

When I add another column, the total goes up by 4 because there is another group of 4.

If I take away a row or column, the total will go down by 4 because I took away a group of 4.

Lesson 7:   Represent arrays and distinguish rows and columns using math
                        drawings.

EUREKA MATH

G2-M6-Lesson 8

1. Create an array with the squares.

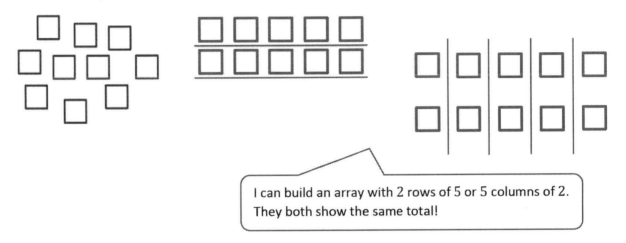

I can build an array with 2 rows of 5 or 5 columns of 2. They both show the same total!

2. Use the array of squares to answer the questions below.

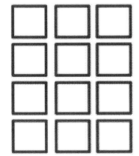

Since there are 3 addends, I know this repeated addition equation relates to the columns.

a. There are __3__ squares in one row.

b. There are __4__ squares in one column.

c. __4__ + __4__ + __4__ = __12__

d. 3 columns of __4__ = __4__ rows of __3__ = __12__ total.

3. Draw a tape diagram to match your repeated addition equation and array.

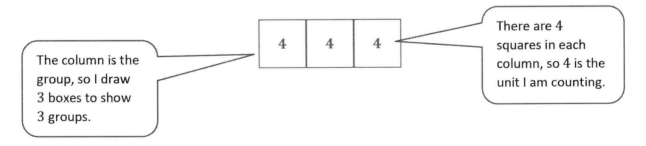

The column is the group, so I draw 3 boxes to show 3 groups.

There are 4 squares in each column, so 4 is the unit I am counting.

G2-M6-Lesson 9

1. Draw an array for each word problem. Write a repeated addition equation to match each array.

    Jason collected some stones. He put them in 5 rows with 3 stones in each row. How many stones did Jason have altogether?

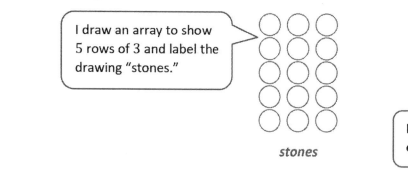

    I draw an array to show 5 rows of 3 and label the drawing "stones."

    $3 + 3 + 3 + 3 + 3 = 15$

    stones

    I write a repeated addition equation to match the array.

    Jason had 15 stones altogether.

    I write a sentence to answer the question.

2. Draw a tape diagram for each word problem. Write a repeated addition equation to match each tape diagram.

    Each of Maria's 4 friends has 5 markers. How many markers do Maria's friends have in all?

    The 4 friends are the groups. I draw 4 boxes to show 4 groups.

    | 5 | 5 | 5 | 5 |

    I write the number 5 in each box to show how many markers each friend has.

    $5 + 5 + 5 + 5 = 20$

    Maria's friends have 20 markers in all.

    I write a repeated addition equation to match the tape diagram and a sentence to answer the question.

10   **Lesson 9:**   Solve word problems involving addition of equal groups in rows and
                                columns.

EUREKA
MATH

G2-M6-Lesson 10

1. Use your square tiles to construct the following rectangles with no gaps or overlaps. Write a repeated addition equation to match each construction.

Construct a rectangle with 2 rows of 3 tiles.   Construct a rectangle with 2 columns of 3 tiles.

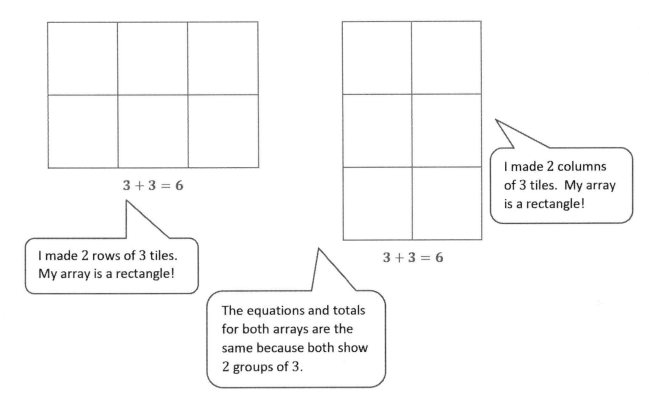

$3 + 3 = 6$

I made 2 rows of 3 tiles. My array is a rectangle!

I made 2 columns of 3 tiles. My array is a rectangle!

$3 + 3 = 6$

The equations and totals for both arrays are the same because both show 2 groups of 3.

2. Construct a rectangle of 4 tiles that has equal rows and columns. Write a repeated addition equation to match.

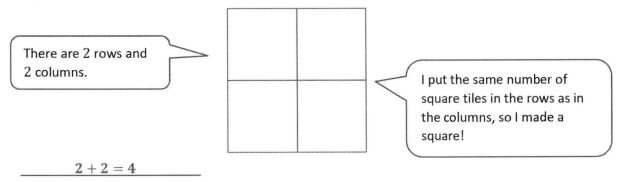

There are 2 rows and 2 columns.

I put the same number of square tiles in the rows as in the columns, so I made a square!

$2 + 2 = 4$

G2-M6-Lesson 11

1. Construct an array with 20 square tiles.

   Write a repeated addition equation to match the array.

   $$5 + 5 + 5 + 5 = 20$$

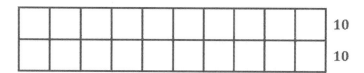

5
5
5
5

   Rearrange the 20 square tiles into a different array.

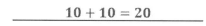

10
10

   Write a repeated addition equation to match the new array.

   $$10 + 10 = 20$$

> I can make an array with 4 rows of 5 tiles and write a repeated addition equation to match. It's easy to skip-count by 5's.

> I can rearrange the tiles to make another array with 2 rows of 10 tiles. I can use my doubles facts to find the total: $10 + 10 = 20$.

2. Construct 2 arrays with 16 square tiles.

   2 rows of __8__ = __16__

   2 rows of __8__ = 8 rows of __2__

> If I turn 2 rows of 8 so they're standing up, I will have 8 rows of 2. I know that $8 + 8$ equals $2 + 2 + 2 + 2 + 2 + 2 + 2 + 2$.

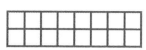 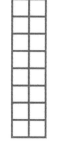

EUREKA MATH™

G2-M6-Lesson 12

1. Trace a square tile to make an array with 3 columns of 4.

It is important for me to be precise when I am tracing a tile to make an array. I can't have gaps or overlaps.

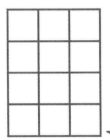

This rectangle shows that I can compose a larger unit from smaller units. Each column is a unit of 4. There are 3 columns of 4, so $4 + 4 + 4 = 12$.

3 columns of 4 = __12__

__4__ + __4__ + __4__ = __12__

2. Complete the following array without gaps or overlaps. The first tile has been drawn for you.

5 rows of 2

First, I can start with the top side of the next square. The length of the line is about the same length as the first tile. Next, I can draw the bottom line of the square to match the length of the top line.

Then, I can close the square by making a third line.

I can continue this pattern to make 4 more rows of 2 directly below the first two squares.

G2-M6-Lesson 13

1. Step 1: Construct a rectangle with 5 columns of 3.

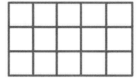

Step 2: Separate 3 columns of 3.

I decompose 5 columns of 3 into 2 smaller rectangles, or parts. 3 columns of 3 and 2 columns of 3 make 5 columns of 3.

Step 3: Write a number bond to show the whole and two parts. Write a repeated addition sentence to match each part of the number bond.

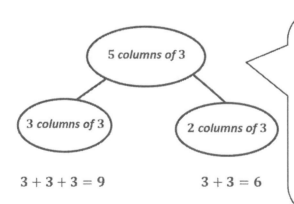

I can draw a number bond to match my arrays. I know that a larger rectangle can be decomposed into smaller rectangles because 15 can be decomposed into 9 and 6.

EUREKA
MATH™

2. Use 16 square tiles to construct a rectangle.

   a. __4__ rows of __4__ = __16__

> I can remove a row, which is a unit of 4, so my new rectangle has 12 square tiles. $4 + 4 + 4 = 12$

   b. Remove 1 row. How many square tiles are there now? __12__

   c. Remove 1 column from the new rectangle you made in part (b). How many square tiles are there now? __9__

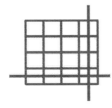

> Now I can remove a column, which is a unit of 3. My new rectangle has 3 fewer square tiles than part (b). $3 + 3 + 3 = 9$

G2-M6-Lesson 14

1. Imagine that you have just cut this rectangle into rows.

    a.   What do you see? Draw a picture.

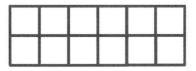

> I can decompose the same rectangle into rows and columns. I can see 2 rows of 6.

How many squares are in each row? ____6____

b.   Imagine that you have just cut this rectangle into columns. What do you see? Draw a picture.

How many squares are in each column? ____2____

> I can also see 6 columns of 2.

2. Create another rectangle using the same number of squares.

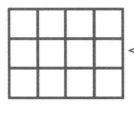

> I can make another rectangle with the same 12 squares. I can rearrange 2 columns of 2 as 1 row of 4. Now, my rectangle has 3 rows of 4.

How many squares are in each row? ____4____

How many squares are in each column? ____3____

16   Lesson 14:   Use scissors to partition a rectangle into same-size squares, and compose
                           arrays with the squares.

©2015 Great Minds. eureka-math.org
G2-M1-HWH-1.3.0-07.2015

EUREKA
MATH

G2-M6-Lesson 15

1. Shade in an array with 5 columns of 4.

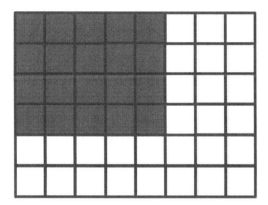

> I can shade 1 column of 4 and then 4 more columns of 4. I can say that each column has a group, or unit, of 4.

Write a repeated addition equation for the array.

$$4 + 4 + 4 + 4 + 4 = 20$$

> I see 5 columns of 4, or 5 fours. I can use doubles to add. $8 + 8 + 4 = 20$. I have shaded 20 squares altogether.

2. Draw one more row and then two more columns to make a new array.

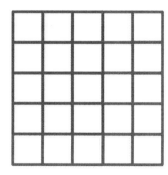

> First, I can draw another row of 3. Now there are 5 rows of 3. Then I can draw 2 more columns. That makes 5 columns of 5 altogether.

Write a repeated addition equation for the new array.

$$5 + 5 + 5 + 5 + 5 = 25$$

> I see 5 columns of 5, or 5 fives. I can skip-count by 5's. There are 25 squares in all.

EUREKA MATH

Lesson 15:   Use math drawings to partition a rectangle with square tiles, and relate to repeated addition.

17

©2015 Great Minds. eureka-math.org
G2-M1-HWH-1.3.0-07.2015

G2-M6-Lesson 16

1. Shade to create a copy of the design on the empty grid.

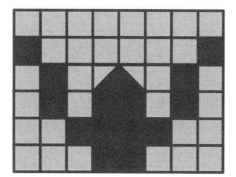   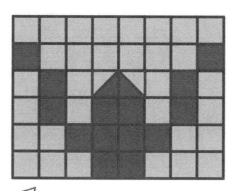

> I can use square tiles to put together and break apart rectangles. Look, I see that some squares are only half-shaded to make triangles! When I make designs, I have to pay close attention to the rows and columns so that I shade in the correct squares.

2. Use colored pencils to create a design in the bolded square section. Create a tessellation by repeating the design throughout.

> The core unit that I am repeating has 3 rows and 3 columns. I can create the same design again by shading in the same pattern. I know that this pattern could go on and on if I kept repeating it.

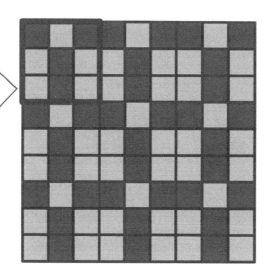

G2-M6-Lesson 17

1. Draw to double the group you see. Complete the sentences, and write an addition equation.

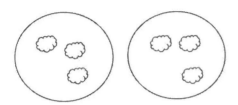

There are __3__ clouds in each group.

__3__ + __3__ = __6__

I know that when both addends are the same, I have doubles. $1 + 1 = 2$, $2 + 2 = 4$, $3 + 3 = 6$, and so on. Doubling a number always makes an even number even when there are 3 objects in each group.

2. Draw an array for the set below. Complete the sentences.

2 rows of 5

2 rows of 5 = __10__

__5__ + __5__ = __10__

There are 5 counters in each group. I can double a row of 5 and write a number sentence to match, $5 + 5 = 10$. When I look at this array, I know right away that there is an even number of objects because I am doubling a number, 5.

5 doubled is __10__.

©2015 Great Minds. eureka-math.org
G2-M1-HWH-1.3.0-07.2015

G2-M6-Lesson 18

1. Pair the objects, and count by twos to decide if the number of objects is even.

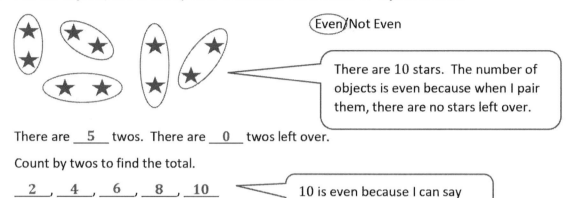

(Even)/Not Even

> There are 10 stars. The number of objects is even because when I pair them, there are no stars left over.

There are __5__ twos. There are __0__ twos left over.

Count by twos to find the total.

__2__, __4__, __6__, __8__, __10__

> 10 is even because I can say 10 when counting by twos.

2. Draw to continue the pattern of the pairs in the space below until you have drawn 10 pairs.

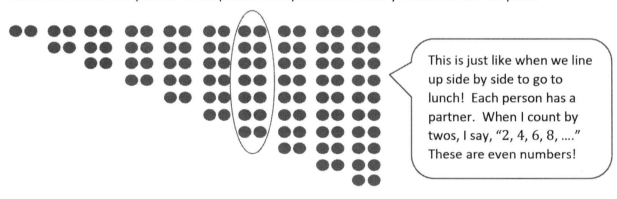

> This is just like when we line up side by side to go to lunch! Each person has a partner. When I count by twos, I say, "2, 4, 6, 8, …." These are even numbers!

3. Write the number of dots in each array in Problem 2 in order from least to greatest.

   2, 4, 6, 8, 10, 12, 14, 16, 18, 20

4. Circle the array in Problem 2 that has 2 columns of 7.

> I can make 2 columns of 7, and $7 + 7 = 14$. Even if one of the numbers I'm adding isn't even, when I double it, I get an even number.

EUREKA MATH

G2-M6-Lesson 19

1. Skip-count the columns in the array. The first one has been done for you.

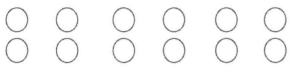

   <u> 2 </u> <u> 4 </u> <u> 6 </u> <u> 8 </u> <u> 10 </u> <u> 12 </u>

   > I can skip-count by 2's using the columns of the array. If I keep adding columns of 2 to this pattern, I can say, "..., 14, 16, 18, 20." There's a pattern in the ones place! 0, 2, 4, 6, 8.

2. Solve.

   $1 + 1 = $ <u> 2 </u> $4 + 4 = $ <u> 8 </u>

   $2 + 2 = $ <u> 4 </u> $5 + 5 = $ <u> 10 </u>

   $3 + 3 = $ <u> 6 </u> $6 + 6 = $ <u> 12 </u>

   > When I find doubles, I see a pattern in the answers; they are skip-counting by 2's.

3. Write to identify the **bold** numbers as *even* or *odd*.

$24 + 1 = 25$	$24 - 1 = 23$
even + 1 = *odd*	*even* − 1 = *odd*

   > When I add 1 to or subtract 1 from an even number, the new number is always odd!

4. Is the **bold** number even or odd? Circle the answer, and explain how you know.

39 even/(odd)	**Explanation:** *This number does not have 0, 2, 4, 6, or 8 in the ones place. I know that 40 is even, so 40 − 1 has to be odd.*

EUREKA MATH™   Lesson 19:   Investigate the pattern of even numbers: 0, 2, 4, 6, and 8 in the ones place, and relate to odd numbers.

©2015 Great Minds. eureka-math.org
G2-M1-HWH-1.3.0-07.2015

21

G2-M6-Lesson 20

1. Use the objects to create an array.

	Array	Redraw your picture with 1 *less* circle.
(scattered circles)	○○○○○○○ ○○○○○○○	○○○○○○○ ○○○○○○
	There are an ~~even~~/odd (circle one) number of circles.	There are an even/~~odd~~ (circle one) number of circles.

If I draw the array with 1 less circle, there are an odd number of circles. Now, I don't see 2 equal groups of 7.

2. Solve. Tell if each number is odd (O) or even (E).

$11 + 13 = \underline{\ 24\ }$

$\underline{\ O\ } + \underline{\ O\ } = \underline{\ E\ }$

I know that 11 and 13 are odd because they do not have 0, 2, 4, 6 , or 8 in the ones place. When I add two odd numbers, I get an even number.

3. Write two examples for each case; next to your answer, write if your answers are even or odd.

Add an even number to an odd number.

$\underline{12 + 7 = 19\ \ odd}$ $\underline{8 + 13 = 21\ \ odd}$

I know that when I add an even number and an odd number, the sum will be odd. I cannot make 2 equal groups with 21 tiles, and I can't count by twos to 21.

EUREKA
MATH

Homework Helpers

Grade 2
Module 7

G2-M7-Lesson 1

1. Count and categorize each picture to complete the table with tally marks.

No Legs	2 Legs	4 Legs
|	|||	|||

> I can count how many animals are in each category. I cross out each animal as I record it with a tally mark under the correct category.

2. Use the Animal Classification table to answer the following questions about the types of animals Ms. Lee's second-grade class found in the local zoo.

Animal Classification			
Birds	Fish	Mammals	Reptiles
6	5	11	3

> I know that this question is asking me to find the total number of birds, fish, or reptiles in the table. It's not asking for the number of categories.

a. How many animals are birds, fish, or reptiles? __14__ $6 + 5 + 3 = 14$

b. How many more birds and mammals are there than fish and reptiles? __9__ $17 - 8 = 9$

c. How many animals were classified? __25__ $6 + 5 + 11 + 3 = 11 + 14 = 25$

EUREKA MATH   Lesson 1:   Sort and record data into a table using up to four categories; use category counts to solve word problems.   1

©2015 Great Minds. eureka-math.org
G2-M1-HWH-1.3.0-07.2015

d. If 5 more birds and 2 more reptiles were added to the table, how many fewer reptiles would there be than birds? __6__

   B $6 + 5 = 11$ $5 + \underline{6} = 11$

   R $3 + 2 = 5$

I can use addition or subtraction when I see the words *how many fewer*.

Lesson 1:   Sort and record data into a table using up to four categories; use category counts to solve word problems.

©2015 Great Minds. eureka-math.org
G2-M1-HWH-1.3.0-07.2015

G2-M7-Lesson 2

1. Use grid paper to create a picture graph below using data provided in the table. Then, answer the questions.

Central Park Zoo Animal Classification			
Birds	Fish	Mammals	Reptiles
6	5	11	3

Title: _Central Park Zoo Animal Classification_

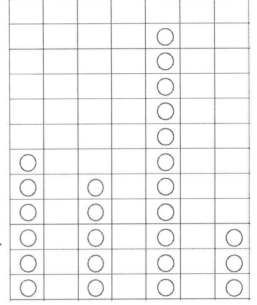

Birds   Fish   Mammals   Reptiles

Legend: _Each ◯ stands for 1 animal_

a. How many more animals are mammals and fish than birds and reptiles? ___7___

$11 + 5 = 16$ $6 + 3 = 9$ $16 - 9 = 7$

b. How many fewer animals are reptiles than mammals? ___8___ $11 - 3 = 8$

> I use the graph to help me answer comparison questions like *how many more* or *how many fewer*.

> I organize the data from the table in a vertical picture graph. I put the categories in the same order as they are in the table, so I don't get confused. I must remember to include a title and a legend.

2. Use the table below to create a picture graph in the space provided.

Animal Habitats		
Desert	Tundra	Grassland
卌 I	卌	卌 卌 IIII

> I draw a circle in each box to represent each animal recorded by a tally mark in the table. Circles help me to draw efficiently, and the legend explains what they represent.

Title: _____ Animal Habitats _____

Desert _____	○ ○ ○ ○ ○ ○
Tundra _____	○ ○ ○ ○ ○
Grassland _____	○ ○ ○ ○ ○ ○ ○ ○ ○ ○ ○ ○ ○ ○

Legend: _____ Each ○ stands for 1 animal _____

a. How many more animals live in the grassland than in the desert? __ 8 __

$$14 - 6 = 8$$

b. How many fewer animals live in the tundra than in the grassland and desert combined? __ 15 __

$$14 + 6 = 20 \qquad 20 - 5 = 15$$

> The first question asks *how many more*. I can figure out the answer by subtracting or by counting the extra circles in the picture graph for the grassland compared to the desert. There are 8 extra circles.

Lesson 2:   Draw and label a picture graph to represent data with up to four categories.

©2015 Great Minds. eureka-math.org
G2-M1-HWH-1.3.0-07.2015

EUREKA MATH

G2-M7-Lesson 3

Complete the bar graph below using data provided in the table.

Animal Habitats		
Desert	**Arctic**	**Grassland**
ⅢⅠ Ⅰ	ⅢⅠ	ⅢⅠ ⅢⅠ ⅢⅠ

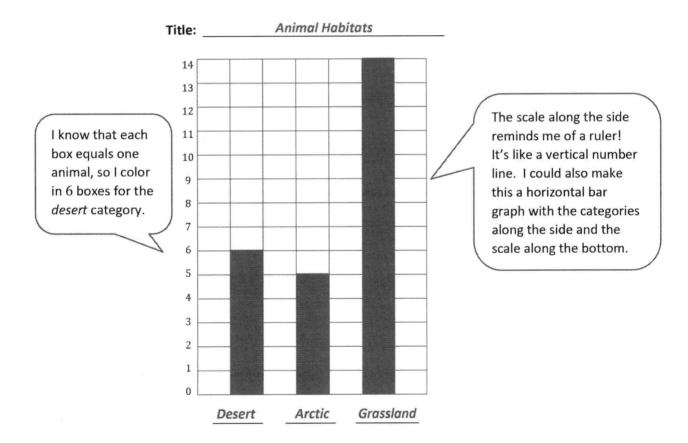

a.   How many total animals are living in the three habitats?   _25_

$$6 + 5 + 14 = 11 + 14 = 25$$

Lesson 3:   Draw and label a bar graph to represent data; relate the count scale to   5
              the number line.

©2015 Great Minds. eureka-math.org
G2-M1-HWH-1.3.0-07.2015

b. How many more animals live in the grassland than in the desert and arctic combined?   __3__

$$6 + 5 = 11 \qquad\qquad 14 - 11 = 3$$

> When I combine the number of boxes I colored for *desert* and *arctic*, I count 11. I look at the graph and see that 11 is 3 fewer boxes than 14, which is the number of animals living in the grassland.

c. If 2 animals were removed from each category, how many animals would there be?   __19__

$$4 + 3 + 12 = 19$$

Lesson 3:   Draw and label a bar graph to represent data; relate the count scale to the number line.

©2015 Great Minds. eureka-math.org
G2-M1-HWH-1.3.0-07.2015

G2-M7-Lesson 4

Complete the bar graph using the table with the types of bugs Alicia counted in the park. Then, answer the following questions.

Types of Bugs			
Butterflies	Spiders	Bees	Grasshoppers
5	14	12	7

> Before I can record the data, I need to write a title for the graph, label the four categories, and write a number scale at the bottom.

Title: ___*Types of Bugs*___

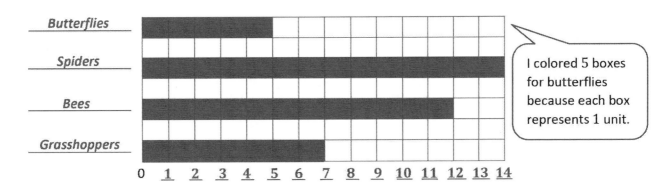

> I colored 5 boxes for butterflies because each box represents 1 unit.

a. How many more bees than grasshoppers were counted in the park? __5__

$$7 + \underline{} = 12$$

b. How many bugs did Alicia count in the park? __38__

$$5 + 14 + 12 + 7 = \underline{}$$
$$19 \quad + \quad 19$$
$$20 + 20 - 2 = 38$$

> I know I can add in any order and use the strategy that works best for me. When I add 19 + 19, I think of adding 20 + 20. But then I have to subtract 2 because each addend is 1 less than 20.

c. How many fewer butterflies than bees and grasshoppers were counted in the park? __14__

$$12 + 7 = 19 \qquad\qquad 19 - 5 = 14$$

> I can answer comparison questions using the data from my graph. Here, I subtracted 19 − 5 = 14. In part (a), I thought of the missing part to solve, 7 + __ = 12. I can use both operations!

G2-M7-Lesson 5

Use the table to complete the bar graph. Then, answer the following questions.

Number of Dimes Donated			
Madison	Ross	Bella	Miguel
15	9	12	11

Title: ___*Number of Dimes Donated*___

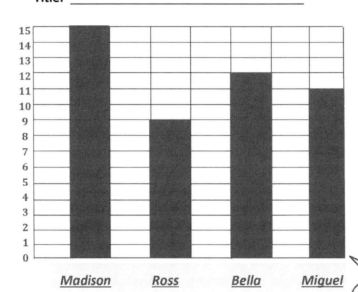

I know that the beginning of the count scale starts at 0, not 1.

a. How many fewer dimes did Bella donate than Ross and Miguel? __8__

$9 + 11 = 20$ $12 + \_\_\_ = 20$

b. How many more dimes are needed for Madison to donate the same as Ross and Bella? __6__

$9 + 12 = 21$ $15 + \_\_\_ = 21$

c. How many dimes were donated in total?   47

$15 + 9 + 12 + 11 = $ ___

      27   20

$27 + 20 = 47$

> I can use mental math to find the total. I can make a ten: $9 + 11 = 20$. It's easy to add the tens and ones when I combine 15 and 12. Then, $27 + 20 = 47$.

d. Circle the pair that has more dimes, Madison and Ross or Bella and Miguel. How many more?

    1

$15 + 9 = 24$ $12 + 11 = 23$ $24 - 23 = 1$

©2015 Great Minds. eureka-math.org
G2-M1-HWH-1.3.0-07.2015

G2-M7-Lesson 6

Count or add to find the total value of each group of coins.

Write the value using the ¢ or $ symbol.

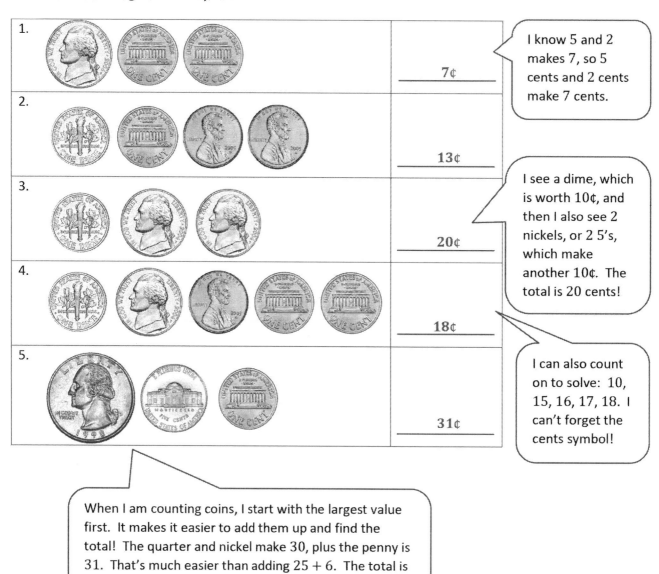

1. _____ 7¢ _____

I know 5 and 2 makes 7, so 5 cents and 2 cents make 7 cents.

2. _____ 13¢ _____

I see a dime, which is worth 10¢, and then I also see 2 nickels, or 2 5's, which make another 10¢. The total is 20 cents!

3. _____ 20¢ _____

4. _____ 18¢ _____

I can also count on to solve: 10, 15, 16, 17, 18. I can't forget the cents symbol!

5. _____ 31¢ _____

When I am counting coins, I start with the largest value first. It makes it easier to add them up and find the total! The quarter and nickel make 30, plus the penny is 31. That's much easier than adding 25 + 6. The total is 31 cents!

©2015 Great Minds. eureka-math.org
G2-M1-HWH-1.3.0-07.2015

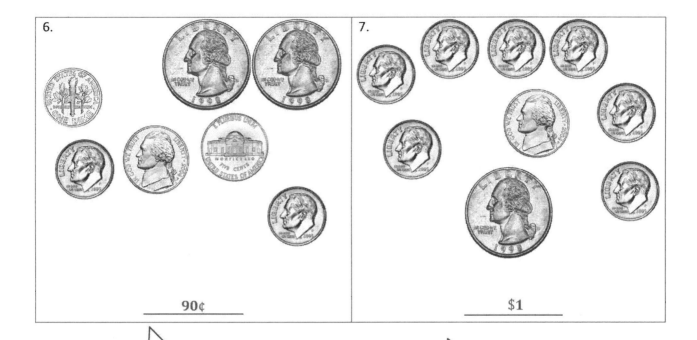

6.

90¢

7.

$1

I know that 2 quarters make
50 cents, so I start there. The
dimes have the next biggest
value, so I add those on. There
are 3 dimes, so I add on 30 cents.
Then there are 2 nickels, so I add
on 10 more cents. The total is
90 cents!

I can make the next ten by
adding the nickel to the quarter.
That makes it easier to add on all
the dimes. $25 + 5 = 30$, and
then I skip-count 40, 50, …, 100.
100 cents is one dollar!

G2-M7-Lesson 7

Solve.

Enrique had 2 quarters, 2 dimes, 5 pennies, and 3 nickels in his wallet. Then, he bought a lemonade for 25 cents. How much money did he have left?

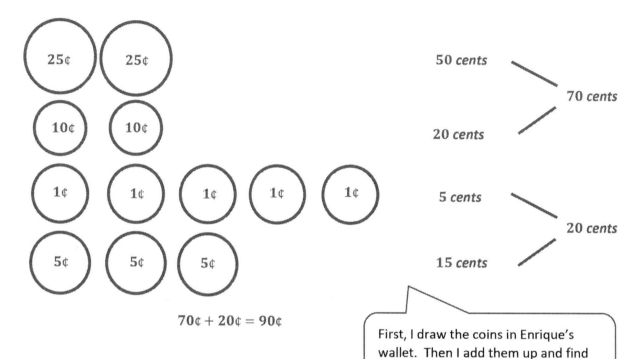

50 *cents*

70 *cents*

20 *cents*

5 *cents*

20 *cents*

15 *cents*

$$70¢ + 20¢ = 90¢$$

First, I draw the coins in Enrique's wallet. Then I add them up and find that he has 90 cents.

90¢

25¢	?

$$90 \xrightarrow{-20} 70 \xrightarrow{-5} 65$$

I draw a tape diagram to show the parts and the whole. The whole is 90 cents. One part is 25 cents for the lemonade. The part Enrique has left is my unknown. I can solve using the arrow way.

$$90¢ - 25¢ = ?$$

$$90¢ - 25¢ = 65¢$$

Enrique had 65 cents left.

EUREKA
MATH

G2-M7-Lesson 8

Solve.

Claire has $89. She has 3 more five-dollar bills, 4 more one-dollar bills, and 1 more ten-dollar bill than Trey. How much money does Trey have?

> First I can draw all the bills that Claire has more than Trey. I add them up and find that she has $29 more than Trey.

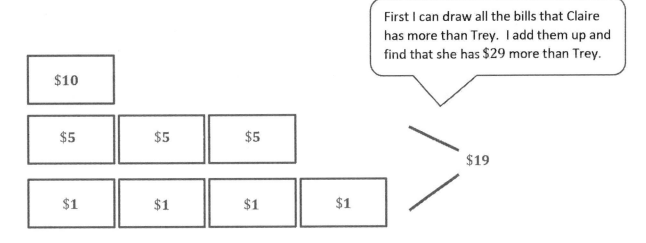

$10 + $19 = $29

> Next, I draw a tape diagram to compare Claire's and Trey's money.

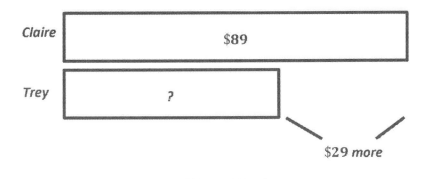

$89 − $29 = ?

Trey has $60.

> Claire has $89, and I know Trey has $29 less than that. I don't know how much Trey has yet, so I put a question mark in the tape that represents Trey's money.

G2-M7-Lesson 9

1. Write another way to make the same total value.

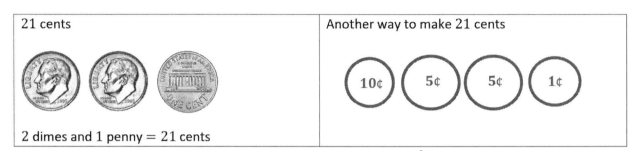

21 cents	Another way to make 21 cents
2 dimes and 1 penny = 21 cents	10¢ 5¢ 5¢ 1¢

I know that 2 nickels makes 10 cents, so I just change 1 dime for 2 nickels. I could have also used some pennies instead of only nickels, but that would take longer to draw because it uses more coins.

I know that 3 quarters is 75 cents. Then I add up the other coins. $10 + 5 + 5 + 5 = 25$, so Andrew has 100 cents, or 1 dollar.

2. Andrew has 3 quarters, 1 dime, 2 nickels, and 5 pennies in his pocket. Write two other coin combinations that would equal the same amount of change.

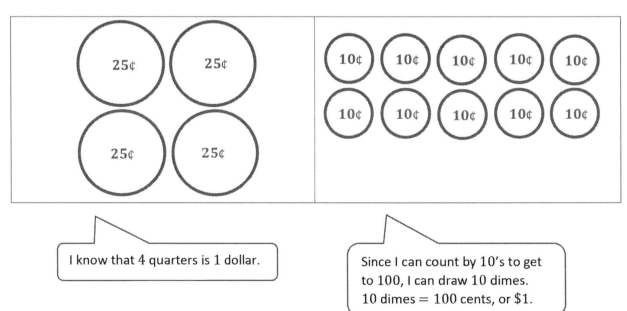

I know that 4 quarters is 1 dollar.

Since I can count by 10's to get to 100, I can draw 10 dimes. 10 dimes = 100 cents, or $1.

Lesson 9:   Solve word problems involving different combinations of coins with the same total value.   **EUREKA MATH**

G2-M7-Lesson 10

1. Ana showed 30 cents two ways. Circle the way that uses the fewest coins.

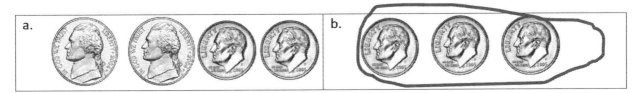

What two coins from part (a) were changed for one coin in part (b)?

Ana changed 2 nickels for 1 dime.

> Ana had 2 nickels, which equal 10 cents, so she was able to change them for 1 dime.

2. Show 74 cents two ways. Use the fewest possible coins on the right below.

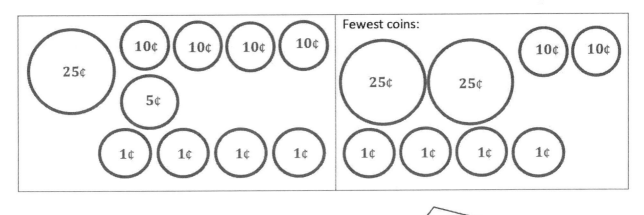

> For the fewest coins, I start with the quarter because it has the highest value. 25, 50, 75. Oops, 3 quarters is too much! I'll stop at 50 cents. Now, I add on the next highest value, dimes. 60, 70. I need 4 cents more, so I add 4 pennies.

3. Shelby made a mistake when asked for two ways to show 66¢. Circle her mistake, and explain what she did wrong.

2 quarters, 1 dime, 1 nickel, 1 penny	Fewest coins:
	6 dimes, 1 nickel, 1 penny

The first combination is the fewest coins. Since 2 quarters have the same value as 5 dimes, Shelby

only needs 5 coins to make 66¢. Her second combination uses 8 coins.

EUREKA
MATH™

G2-M7-Lesson 11

1. Count up using the arrow way to complete each number sentence. Then, use coins to check your answers, if possible.

    65¢ + ___35¢___ = 100¢

    $$65 \xrightarrow{+5} 70 \xrightarrow{+30} 100$$

    > I start at 65 cents and add 5 more to get to the next 10, which is 70 cents. I know I need 30 more cents to get to 100 cents, or $1. 5 + 30 = 35, so the missing part is 35 cents.

2. Solve using the arrow way and a number bond.

    22¢ + ___78¢___ = 100¢

    $$22 \xrightarrow{+8} 30 \xrightarrow{+70} 100$$

    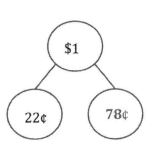

    > I use the number bond to show that the whole is $1, and there are two parts. The part I know already is 22 cents. After I solve using the arrow way, I can fill in the missing part, which is 78 cents.

    100¢ − 65¢ = ___35¢___

    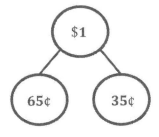

    $$100 \xrightarrow{-60} 40 \xrightarrow{-5} 35$$

    > I use the arrow way to subtract, too! If I buy something for 65 cents, and I give the cashier 1 dollar, I will get 35 cents in change!

G2-M7-Lesson 12

Maria has 1 quarter, 8 pennies, 4 nickels, and 1 dime. She needs $1 to ride the bus. How much should Maria borrow from her mom?

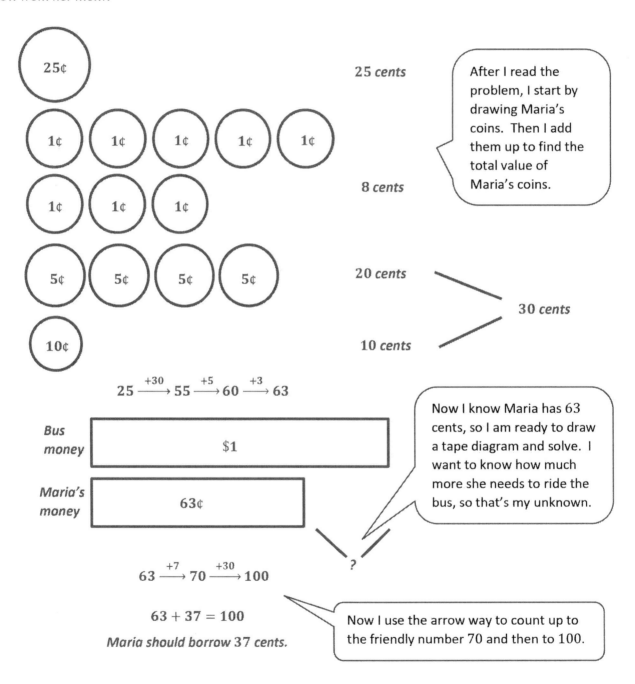

25 cents

8 cents

20 cents
30 cents
10 cents

After I read the problem, I start by drawing Maria's coins. Then I add them up to find the total value of Maria's coins.

$25 \xrightarrow{+30} 55 \xrightarrow{+5} 60 \xrightarrow{+3} 63$

Bus money $1

Maria's money   63¢

Now I know Maria has 63 cents, so I am ready to draw a tape diagram and solve. I want to know how much more she needs to ride the bus, so that's my unknown.

?

$63 \xrightarrow{+7} 70 \xrightarrow{+30} 100$

$63 + 37 = 100$

Maria should borrow 37 cents.

Now I use the arrow way to count up to the friendly number 70 and then to 100.

EUREKA
MATH™

©2015 Great Minds. eureka-math.org
G2-M1-HWH-1.3.0-07.2015

G2-M7-Lesson 13

James had 1 quarter, 1 dime, and 12 pennies. He found 3 coins under his bed. Now he has 77 cents. What 3 coins did he find?

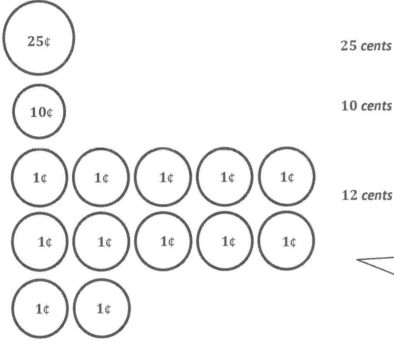

25 *cents*

10 *cents*

12 *cents*

After I read the problem, I draw the coins that James had at first. Then I add them up to find the total using the arrow way. James had 47 cents.

$$25 \xrightarrow{+10} 35 \xrightarrow{+10} 45 \xrightarrow{+2} 47$$

$$47 + \underline{\quad 30 \quad} = 77$$

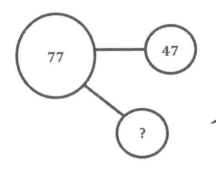

When I show it this way, in a number bond with a missing part, it helps me understand the situation. He found 30 cents more because $47 + 30 = 77$. I know because only the tens change from 47 to 77. 77 is 3 tens more than 47.

James found 3 dimes.

I know that James found 30 cents, and 30 is 3 tens, so he must have found 3 dimes!

EUREKA
MATH™   **Lesson 13:**   Solve two-step word problems involving dollars or cents with totals   19
                             within $100 or $1.

©2015 Great Minds. eureka-math.org
G2-M1-HWH-1.3.0-07.2015

G2-M7-Lesson 14

1. Measure these objects found in your home with an inch tile. Record the measurements in the table provided.

Object	Measurement
Length of a hairbrush	4 *inches*
Height of a milk carton	10 *inches*
Length of the oven	27 *inches*

> I put the tile at one end of the milk carton and make a mark where the tile begins and ends. Then, I move the tile forward and place the edge right on top of the previous hash mark.

> Since I can't draw on an oven, I used the tip of my pencil to remind me where to place my inch tile each time. The spaces between my hash marks are the same length each time.

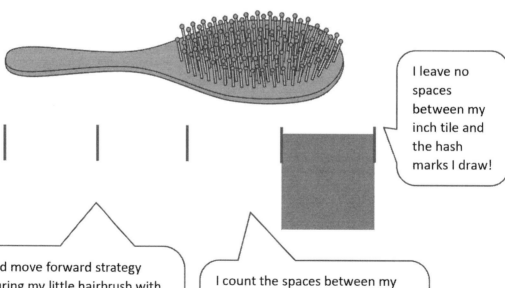

> I leave no spaces between my inch tile and the hash marks I draw!

> I use the mark and move forward strategy when I am measuring my little hairbrush with my red inch tile. I put my inch tile down touching the endpoint of the hairbrush. Then I make a mark where the inch tile ends so I know where to place it when I move it over.

> I count the spaces between my hash marks to see how many inches long my hairbrush is. My hairbrush is almost 4 inches, so I can say it's about 4 inches.

Lesson 14:   Connect measurement with physical units by using iteration with an inch tile to measure.

©2015 Great Minds. eureka-math.org
G2-M1-HWH-1.3.0-07.2015

EUREKA MATH

2. Charlene measures her pencil with her inch tile. She marks off where each inch ends so she knows where to place the tile. Charlene says the pencil is 4 inches long.

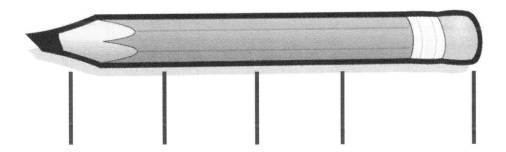

Is Charlene's measurement correct? Explain your answer.

It looks like Charlene did not start her measurement in the correct place. The first hash mark is not

lined up with the endpoint of the pencil. It also looks like she was not careful with her measuring

because the last hash mark looks farther than an inch from the one before. She is not correct.

3. Use your inch tile to measure the pencil. How many inch tiles long is the pencil? Explain how you know.

I was very careful to start at the tip of the pencil. I made a hash mark at the endpoint of the

pencil. I used the mark and move forward strategy and was careful not to leave any space

between my tile and my hash marks. The pencil is about 5 inches long.

EUREKA
MATH™

Lesson 14:   Connect measurement with physical units by using iteration with an inch
              tile to measure.

©2015 Great Minds. eureka-math.org
G2-M1-HWH-1.3.0-07.2015

21

G2-M7-Lesson 15

1. Measure the length of the object with your ruler, and then use your ruler to draw a line equal to the length of the object in the space provided.

> When I measure my toothbrush, I line up the end of the toothbrush with the 0 on my ruler. The end of the handle is even with the 0 on my ruler.

   a. A toothbrush is ____6____ inches.

   b. Draw a line that is the same length as the toothbrush.

   _____

> When I draw my line, I start at 0 and stop after 6 length units. My line is 6 inches long!

2. Measure another household object.

   a. A ____bar of soap____ is ___4___ inches.

   b. Draw a line that is the same length as the ____bar of soap____.

   _____

3.
> I can tell the toothbrush is longer just by looking at the objects or the lines I drew. But to know how much longer it is, I can subtract! $6 - 4 = 2$, so the soap is 2 inches shorter.

   a. Which object was longer? ____toothbrush____

   b. Which object was shorter? ____bar of soap____

   c. The difference between the longer object and the shorter object is ___2___ inches.

©2015 Great Minds. eureka-math.org
G2-M1-HWH-1.3.0-07.2015

4. Measure and label the length of each side of the shape in inches using your ruler.

a. The longest side of the rectangle is ___4___ inches.

b. The shortest side of the rectangle is ___1___ inch.

> To find the difference, I just subtract! $4 - 1 = 3$

c. The longest side of the rectangle is ___3___ inches longer than the shortest side of the rectangle.

> Measuring objects with my ruler is so much quicker than using an inch tile! It's like all the tiles are connected!

G2-M7-Lesson 16

1. Circle the unit that would best measure each object.

Length of a window	inch / (foot) / yard
Height of an office building	inch / foot / (yard)
Length of a shoe	(inch) / foot / yard

> I have to think about how long each object is. If it is very, very long, then I know I should use yards to measure because it is more efficient. It would take a very long time to measure an office building in inches, and that means you could make a lot more mistakes!

> I can picture a yardstick in my mind. I know that an airplane is way longer! I think the guitar is about the length of a yardstick because I can hold it in my arms the same way I can hold a yardstick.

2. Circle the correct estimate for each object.

   a. The length of an airplane is (more than) / less than / about the same as the length of a yardstick.

   b. The length of a guitar is more than / less than / (about the same as) the length of a yardstick.

   c. The height of a coffee mug is more than / (less than) / about the same as the length of a 12-inch ruler.

Lesson 16: Measure various objects using inch rulers and yardsticks.

©2015 Great Minds. eureka-math.org
G2-M1-HWH-1.3.0-07.2015

3. Name 3 objects that you find outside. Decide which unit you would use to measure that object. Record it in the chart in a full statement.

Object	Unit
oak tree	I would use _____yards_____ to measure the height of an __oak tree__.
flower	I would use inches to measure the height of a flower.
park bench	I would use feet to measure the height of a park bench.

I tried to choose objects that I measure in different units. The tree is big so that works for yards. The park bench could also be measured in yards, but if I measure it in feet, I can give a more accurate measurement.

©2015 Great Minds. eureka-math.org
G2-M1-HWH-1.3.0-07.2015

G2-M7-Lesson 17

Estimate the length of each item by using a mental benchmark. Then, measure the item using feet, inches, or yards.

Item	Mental Benchmark	Estimation	Actual Length
Length of a car	*Yardstick or width of a door*	*6 yards*	*5 yards*
Length of the kitchen sink	*Piece of paper*	*2 feet*	*almost 3 feet*
Length of a pen cap	*Quarter*	*1 inch*	*about an inch*

I choose to use the yardstick as my mental benchmark to estimate the length of the car because the car is very long.

I use the paper to estimate the length of the sink because a piece of paper is my mental benchmark for a foot.

I am so close on my estimate of the length of the pen cap! It is easy to picture it next to the quarter, so I estimate 1 inch. The pen cap is just a little longer than 1 inch, so it's about 1 inch.

Lesson 17:   Develop estimation strategies by applying prior knowledge of length and using mental benchmarks.

©2015 Great Minds. eureka-math.org
G2-M1-HWH-1.3.0-07.2015

EUREKA MATH

G2-M7-Lesson 18

1. Measure the lines in inches and centimeters. Round the measurements to the nearest inch or centimeter.

   _____5_____ centimeters   _____2_____ inches

   > Centimeters are smaller, so it takes more of them to cover the length of the line.

2.
   a. Draw a line that is 3 centimeters in length.

   > An inch is longer than a centimeter, so of course my line that is 3 inches is longer than my line that is 3 centimeters!

   b. Draw a line that is 3 inches in length.

3. Sam drew a line that is 11 centimeters long. Susan drew a line that is 8 inches long. Susan thinks her line is shorter than Sam's because 8 is less than 11. Explain why Susan's reasoning is incorrect.

   Susan's reasoning is incorrect because inches are longer than centimeters. You have to look

   at the unit to figure out which line will be longer. An inch is a larger length unit, so Susan's

   line is longer even though 8 is a smaller number.

EUREKA MATH   Lesson 18:   Measure an object twice using different length units and compare; relate measurement to unit size.   27

©2015 Great Minds. eureka-math.org
G2-M1-HWH-1.3.0-07.2015

G2-M7-Lesson 19

1. Measure each set of lines in inches, and write the length on the line. Complete the comparison sentence.

    Line A

    _____ 2 inches _____

    Line B _____ 6 inches _____

    Line A measured about __2__ inches.   Line B measured about __6__ inches.

    Line B is about __4__ inches longer than Line A.

    > To compare the difference in length, I can subtract
    > $6 - 2 = 4$, or I can say $2 + 4 = 6$. Either way, I
    > know that the difference is 4 inches!

2. Solve. Check your answers with a related addition or subtraction sentence.

    a. 9 inches $-$ 7 inches = __2__ inches

        __2__ inches + 7 inches = 9 inches

        > I think of a number bond. Since I
        > know the total and one part, I can
        > figure out the other part. I can think
        > of addition or subtraction to solve!

    b. 9 centimeters + __7__ centimeters = 16 centimeters

        16 centimeters $-$ 7 centimeters = 9 centimeters

Lesson 19:   Measure to compare the differences in lengths using inches, feet, and yards.

©2015 Great Minds. eureka-math.org
G2-M1-HWH-1.3.0-07.2015

EUREKA MATH

G2-M7-Lesson 20

Solve using tape diagrams. Use a symbol for the unknown.

1. Angela knitted 18 inches of a scarf. She wants her scarf to be 1 yard long. How many more inches does Angela need to knit?

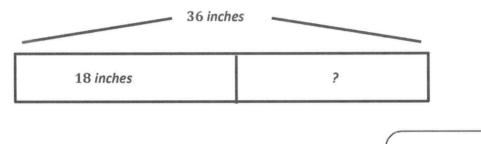

$$36 - 18 = 18$$

> I know that a yard is 36 inches long. The scarf is one yard, so that is my whole. The part I know is the 18 inches that she already knitted.

$$18 \xrightarrow{+2} 20 \xrightarrow{+10} 30 \xrightarrow{+6} 36$$

> I use the arrow way to find the missing part. I add $2 + 10 + 6 = 18$.

Angela needs to knit 18 more inches to finish her scarf.

EUREKA MATH   **Lesson 20:**   Solve two-digit addition and subtraction word problems involving length   **29**
                                by using tape diagrams and writing equations to represent the problem.

©2015 Great Minds. eureka-math.org
G2-M1-HWH-1.3.0-07.2015

2. The total length of all three sides of a triangle is 100 feet. Two sides of the triangle are the same length. One of the equal sides measures 40 feet. What is the length of the side that is not equal?

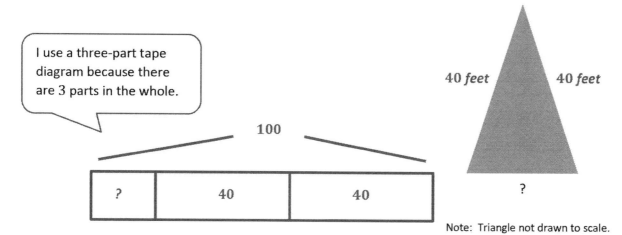

Note: Triangle not drawn to scale.

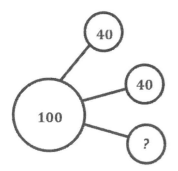

The problem tells me that all the sides together equal 100 feet, so I know that $40 + 40 + ? = 100$. That is what I show in my tape diagram and my number bond.

$40 + 40 + ? = 100$

The length of the third side is 20 feet.

$40 + 40 = 80$. I think, 80 plus what number equals 100? 20. The missing part is 20.

Lesson 20:   Solve two-digit addition and subtraction word problems involving length by using tape diagrams and writing equations to represent the problem.

EUREKA MATH

©2015 Great Minds. eureka-math.org
G2-M1-HWH-1.3.0-07.2015

G2-M7-Lesson 21

Find the value of the point on each part of the meter strip marked by a letter. For each number line, one unit is the distance from one hash mark to the next. (Note: Number lines not drawn to scale.)

1. 25 cm   K   175 cm

Each unit has a length of _____25_____ centimeters.

K = ____100 cm____

To find the value of each unit, I first have to find the difference between the endpoints: $175 - 25 = 150$. The distance is 150. Since there are 6 equal units, I try counting by 10, but that is too small. Let me try counting by 25. I touch each hash mark as I go: 25, 50, 75, 100, 125, 150, 175. It works! K is right in the middle at 100 cm.

2. Each hash mark represents 15 more on the number line.

600   X   Y

What is the difference between X and Y? _____45_____

X = _____615_____

Y = _____660_____

I can find the difference between X and Y by counting by 15. 15, 30, 45. I can also see that there are 3 units between X and Y, and $15 + 15 + 15 = 45$.

I start at 600 and count by 15 to find the value at each hash mark.

 Lesson 21: Identify unknown numbers on a number line diagram by using the distance between numbers and reference points.   31

©2015 Great Minds. eureka-math.org
G2-M1-HWH-1.3.0-07.2015

G2-M7-Lesson 22

1. Each unit length on both number lines is 20 feet. (Note: The number lines are not drawn to scale.)

   a. Show 60 feet more than 80 feet on the number line.

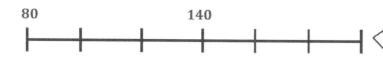

   > I can show 60 more feet on the number line by labeling the endpoint on the left 80 and then counting on 20, 40, 60. It is the same as adding $80 + 60$.

   b. Write an addition sentence to match the number line.

   $$80 + 60 = 140$$

   c. Show 80 feet less than 125 feet on the number line.

   > I start by labeling the endpoint on the right. Then I count down by 20's 4 times since it's 80 feet less. Each time, I touch a hash mark on the number line.

   d. Write a subtraction sentence to match the number line.

   $$125 - 80 = 45$$

EUREKA
MATH™

2. Santiago's meter strip got cut off at 49 centimeters. To measure the length of his eraser, he writes "54 cm − 49 cm." Shirley says it's easier to move the eraser over 1 centimeter. What will Shirley's subtraction sentence be? Explain why she is correct.

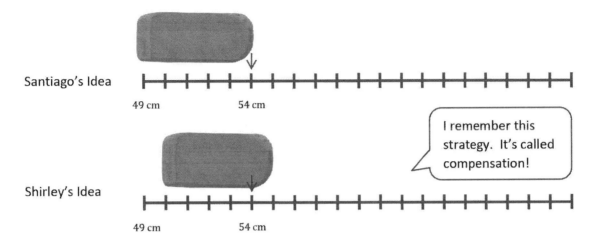

Santiago's Idea

49 cm   54 cm

I remember this strategy. It's called compensation!

Shirley's Idea

49 cm   54 cm

Shirley's subtraction sentence is 55 − 50 = 5. She knows she can move the eraser on the number line, and the length will stay the same. By moving it one unit to the right, she makes an easier problem to solve. 54 − 49 also equals 5, but it's easier to subtract a friendly number like 50 because she only has to subtract the tens.

EUREKA MATH™   Lesson 22:   Represent two-digit sums and differences involving length by using the ruler as a number line.   33

©2015 Great Minds. eureka-math.org
G2-M1-HWH-1.3.0-07.2015

G2-M7-Lesson 23

1. Measure the length of your shoe and record the length here: _about 7 inches_

    Then, measure the length of your family members' shoes, and write the lengths below.

Name:	Shoe Length:
Mom	10 inches
Dad	11 inches
Isaiah (brother)	about 9 inches
Karen (sister)	about 7 inches

> I was very careful to measure everyone's shoe starting at 0 on my ruler.

> My sister's shoe is a little shorter than 7 inches, and my shoe is a little longer than 7 inches, so both our shoes are about 7 inches.

2. Record your data using tally marks on the table provided.

Shoe Length	Tally of Number of People
Shorter than 9 inches	||
About 9 inches	|
Longer than 9 inches	||

a. How many more people have a shoe shorter than 9 inches than have a shoe about equal to 9 inches?

    1 person

b. What is the least common shoe length?

    about 9 inches

c. Ask and answer one comparison question that can be answered using the data above.

Question: _How many fewer people have a shoe that is about 9 inches than is longer than 9 inches?_

Answer: _1 person_

EUREKA MATH

G2-M7-Lesson 24

Use the data in the table to create a line plot and answer the questions.

> First, I look at the data and count how many pencils there are for each length.

Pencil Length (in inches)	Number of Pencils
2	ll
3	l
4	┼┼┼┼
5	┼┼┼┼ ll
6	┼┼┼┼ l
7	
8	l

> Next, I make a number line. I include all the numbers between the shortest and longest lengths, even though no pencils measured 7 inches. All of my intervals must be equal.

> Then I put one X for each pencil. There is 1 pencil with a length of 3 inches, so I put only 1 X above the 3.

Length of Pencils in Mr. Murray's Class

```
                        x
                        x     x
                  x     x     x
                  x     x     x
                  x     x     x
            x     x     x     x
            x     x     x     x           x
        ┼───┼───┼───┼───┼───┼───┼───┼───┼
        1   2   3   4   5   6   7   8   9
```

Pencil Length (in inches)

Describe the pattern you see in the line plot.

The most common pencil length is 5 inches, but 4 inches and 6 inches are also common.

Most of the X's are in the middle of the line plot.

Create your own comparison question related to the data.

How many fewer pencils have a length of 4 inches than a length of 5 inches?

 EUREKA MATH   Lesson 24:   Draw a line plot to represent the measurement data; relate the   35
                                 measurement scale to the number line.

©2015 Great Minds. eureka-math.org
G2-M1-HWH-1.3.0-07.2015

G2-M7-Lesson 25

Use the data in the table provided to create line plots and answer questions.
The table shows the lengths of the daisy chains made at a birthday party.

Length of Daisy Chains	Number of Daisy Chains
3 inches	8
4 inches	5
5 inches	6
7 inches	1
9 inches	3
11 inches	2

> I draw X's above each length to show the data from the table. So I put 8 X's above 3 inches since there are 8 daisy chains that are 3 inches.

> I draw a number line that starts at 3 inches and ends at 11 inches. Since my starting point is 3, I draw a double hash mark to show that the numbers between 0 and 3 are not shown on the scale.

Title _____ **Lengths of Daisy Chains** _____

Line Plot *(in inches)*

> I give my line plot a title, and I label the unit of measure, inches.

a. How many daisy chains were made? _____ 25 _____

b. Draw a conclusion about the data in the line plot.

It is easier to make a short daisy chain. Most of the daisy chains are 5 inches or less.

EUREKA MATH

c. If 5 more people made 7-inch daisy chains and 6 more people made 9-inch daisy chains, how would it change how the line plot looks?

If 5 more people made 7- inch daisy chains and 6 more people made 9- inch daisy chains, then a

9-inch chain would be most common, and an 11- inch chain would be least common.

Lesson 25:   Draw a line plot to represent a given data set; answer questions and draw conclusions based on measurement data.   37

©2015 Great Minds. eureka-math.org
G2-M1-HWH-1.3.0-07.2015

G2-M7-Lesson 26

Use the data in the table provided to create a line plot and answer the questions. Plot only the heights of participants given.

The table below describes the heights of pre-schoolers in the soccer game.

Height of Pre-schoolers (in inches)	Number of Pre-schoolers
35	2
37	3
38	6
39	7
40	5
41	2
42	2

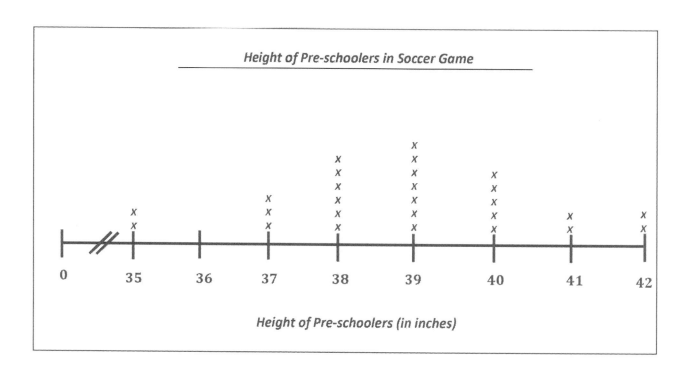

1. How many pre-schoolers were measured? _____27_____

> I started adding with the bigger numbers. I know that $6 + 7 = 13$. Then $13 + 5 = 18$, and 2 more is 20. All that is left is $3 + 2 + 2 = 7$. And $20 + 7 = 27$.

2. How many more pre-schoolers are 38 or 39 inches than 37 or 40 inches? _____5_____

> I know that 13 pre-schoolers are 38 inches or 39 inches, and 8 pre-schoolers are 37 or 40 inches, so then I just subtract. $13 - 8 = 5$, so the answer is 5 pre-schoolers.

3. Draw a conclusion as to why zero pre-schoolers were between 0 and 35 inches.

   There were 0 pre-schoolers less than 35 inches, because most pre-schoolers are more than 35 inches.

   It would be hard to play on a soccer team if you were only 25 inches tall. That's like a baby!

4. For this data, a **line plot** / table (circle one) is easier to read because …

   It is easy to see which heights had the most and least number of pre-schoolers by looking at the number of X's. Also, the measurements are close together, so it's easy to make the number line.

EUREKA MATH   Lesson 26: Draw a line plot to represent a given data set; answer questions and draw conclusions based on measurement data.   39

©2015 Great Minds. eureka-math.org
G2-M1-HWH-1.3.0-07.2015

Homework Helpers

Grade 2
Module 8

G2-M8-Lesson 1

1. Identify the number of sides and angles for the shape. Circle the angles.

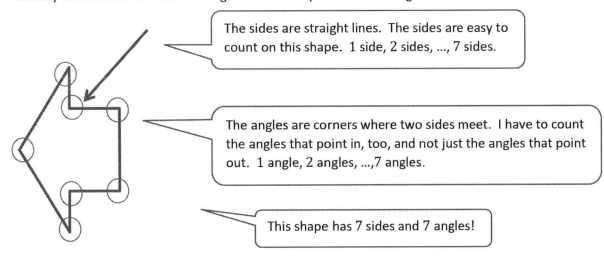

The sides are straight lines. The sides are easy to count on this shape. 1 side, 2 sides, ..., 7 sides.

The angles are corners where two sides meet. I have to count the angles that point in, too, and not just the angles that point out. 1 angle, 2 angles, ...,7 angles.

This shape has 7 sides and 7 angles!

2. Ethan says that this shape has 6 sides and 6 angles. Frankie says that it has 8 sides and 8 angles. Who is correct? How do you know?

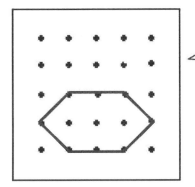

I know that Ethan is correct because I can count 6 sides. I see 3 sides on the top and 3 sides on the bottom. Then I count the angles. I see 3 angles on the left and 3 angles on the right. That means there are 6 sides and 6 angles.

G2-M8-Lesson 2

1. Count the number of sides and angles to identify the polygon.

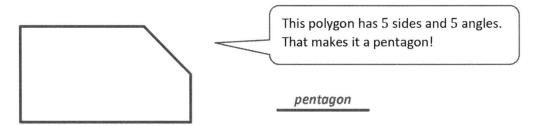

This polygon has 5 sides and 5 angles.
That makes it a pentagon!

pentagon

2. Draw more sides to complete 2 examples of the polygon.

	Example 1	Example 2
Pentagon For each example, __3__ lines were added. A pentagon has ___5___ total sides.		

3. Explain why both polygons C and D are triangles.

Both polygons have 3 sides and 3 angles.

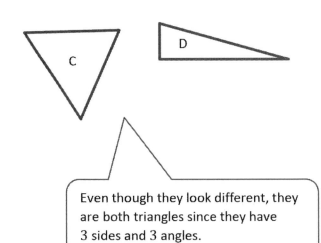

Even though they look different, they are both triangles since they have 3 sides and 3 angles.

Lesson 2:   Build, identify, and analyze two-dimensional shapes with specified attributes.   **EUREKA MATH**

G2-M8-Lesson 3

1. Use a straightedge to draw the polygon with the given attributes.

   Draw a polygon with 3 angles.

   Number of sides: _____3_____

   Name of polygon: _____*triangle*_____

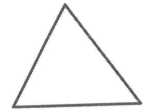

   When I draw a polygon with 3 angles, it also has 3 sides. That is a triangle!

2. Use your straightedge to draw 2 new examples of the polygon you drew for Problem 1.

   Triangle

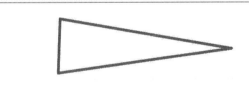   

   All triangles must have 3 sides and 3 angles. By changing the size of the angles and the length of the sides, I can make all kinds of different triangles! This one is long and skinny!

                                     quadrilaterals, pentagons, and hexagons.

                   ©2015 Great Minds. eureka-math.org
                   G2-M1-HWH-1.3.0-07.2015

G2-M8-Lesson 4

1. Use your ruler to draw 2 parallel lines that are not the same length.

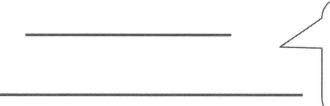

> I know that parallel lines go in the same direction and never touch. I can draw parallel lines by placing my ruler on the paper and using both sides to draw 2 straight lines.

2. Draw a quadrilateral with 4 square corners.

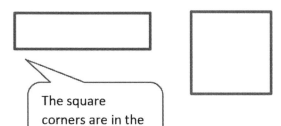

> The square corners are in the shape of an L.

> Both of these quadrilaterals have 4 square corners. That means both shapes are rectangles. The one on the right is a special rectangle called a square! It has 4 square corners *and* 4 sides that are the same length!

3. Draw a quadrilateral with two sets of parallel sides.

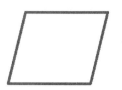

> I know this is a quadrilateral because it has 4 sides and 4 angles. It has no square corners, so it can't be a rectangle. It does have 2 sets of parallel sides; it must be a parallelogram!

Lesson 4:   Use attributes to identify and draw different quadrilaterals including rectangles, rhombuses, parallelograms, and trapezoids.

EUREKA
MATH

G2-M8-Lesson 5

Draw a cube.

Step 1:

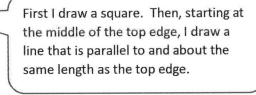

First I draw a square. Then, starting at the middle of the top edge, I draw a line that is parallel to and about the same length as the top edge.

Step 2:

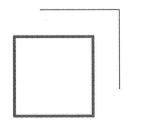

Next, I make a square corner with the right side parallel to the right edge.

Step 3:

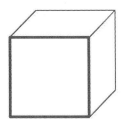

Finally, I draw three lines to connect the three corners of the square face to the endpoints and corner of the lines I drew.

I count the edges by pointing to the ones I see and pointing to the ones I know are hiding! I count 12 edges!

The corners are sharp. There are 4 corners on the front face and 4 corners on the back face. Together that makes 8 corners.

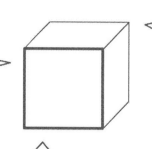

I see 3 faces, and I know 3 are hiding so that makes 6 altogether.

6   **Lesson 5:**   Relate the square to the cube, and describe the cube based on
                              attributes.

G2-M8-Lesson 6

1. Identify each polygon labeled in the tangram as precisely as possible in the space below.

   a. _____*triangle*_____

   b. _____*parallelogram*_____

   c. _____*square*_____

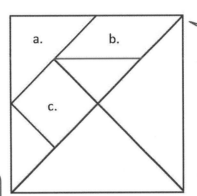

I know letter b is a parallelogram because it has 2 sets of parallel sides but no square corners! 3 sides and 3 angles makes a triangle!

I know letter c is a square. It has 4 square corners, 2 sets of parallel sides, and all the sides are equal in length!

2. Use the parallelogram and the two smallest triangles to make the following polygons. Draw them in the space provided.

   a. A quadrilateral with 1 pair of parallel sides

   Look, I made a trapezoid! It has 4 straight sides, but they're not all the same length. I know it's a trapezoid because it has at least one pair of parallel sides.

   b. A quadrilateral with no square corners

   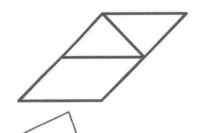

   I know this one is a parallelogram. It has 2 pairs of parallel sides and no square corners. I can see a trapezoid hiding inside!

EUREKA MATH   **Lesson 6:**   Combine shapes to create a composite shape; create a new shape from composite shapes.   **7**

©2015 Great Minds. eureka-math.org
G2-M1-HWH-1.3.0-07.2015

G2-M8-Lesson 7

1. Solve the following puzzle using your tangram pieces. Draw your solutions in the space below.

Use the two smallest triangles to make one larger triangle.

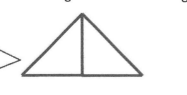

The two small triangles that I use to make one big triangle are the same size. That means this triangle has two equal shares, or two halves!

2. Circle the shapes that show thirds.

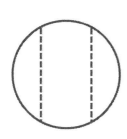 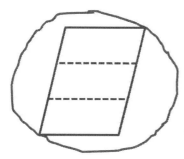 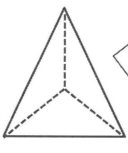

I know this triangle is not cut into thirds because all three parts are not equal shares. The bottom part is bigger than the other ones!

3. Examine the rectangle.

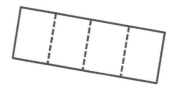

   a. How many equal shares does the rectangle have? ___4___

   b. How many fourths are in the rectangle? ___4___

Lesson 7:   Interpret equal shares in composite shapes as halves, thirds, and fourths.

©2015 Great Minds. eureka-math.org
G2-M1-HWH-1.3.0-07.2015

G2-M8-Lesson 8

1. Name the pattern block used to cover half the rectangle. _____*square*_____

   Sketch the 2 pattern blocks used to cover both halves of the rectangle.

> I can cover the rectangle with 2 squares. The 2 equal shares, or halves, make one whole rectangle.

2. Draw 2 lines to make 3 triangles in the trapezoid below.

> Knowing that a triangle has 3 sides helps me figure out where to draw my lines.

   a. Shade 1 triangle. Each triangle is 1 _____*third*_____ (half / third / fourth) of the whole trapezoid.

   b. Shade 1 more triangle. Now, 2 _____*thirds*_____ (halves / thirds / fourths) of the whole trapezoid are shaded.

   c. Shade 1 more triangle. ___3___ thirds is equal to 1 whole.

> If 2 thirds of the trapezoid are shaded, I have 1 third left to shade. Then, 3 thirds will be shaded. That's 1 whole!

G2-M8-Lesson 9

1. Circle the shapes that have 2 equal shares with 1 share shaded.

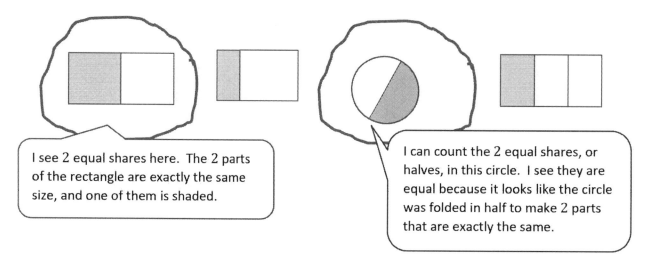

I see 2 equal shares here. The 2 parts of the rectangle are exactly the same size, and one of them is shaded.

I can count the 2 equal shares, or halves, in this circle. I see they are equal because it looks like the circle was folded in half to make 2 parts that are exactly the same.

2. Shade 1 half of the shapes that are split into 2 equal shares. One has been done for you.

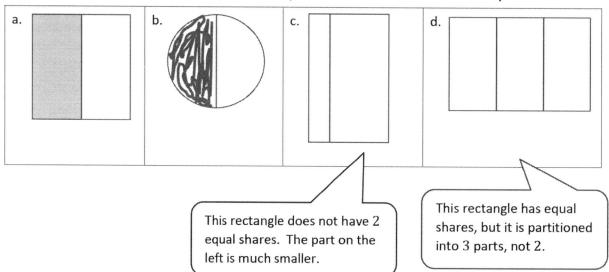

This rectangle does not have 2 equal shares. The part on the left is much smaller.

This rectangle has equal shares, but it is partitioned into 3 parts, not 2.

Lesson 9:   Partition circles and rectangles into equal parts, and describe those parts as halves, thirds, or fourths.

EUREKA MATH™

3. Partition the shapes to show halves. Shade 1 half of each. Compare your halves to your partner's.

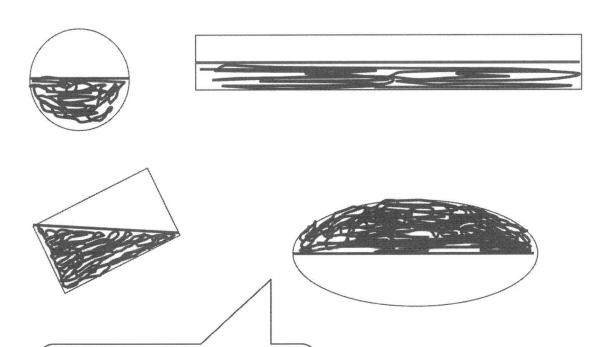

I can partition, or divide, the shape into halves by drawing a line right through the center, as if I have folded the shape in half. Then, I shade in 1 of the 2 equal shares.

EUREKA
MATH™

Lesson 9:   Partition circles and rectangles into equal parts, and describe those parts
              as halves, thirds, or fourths.

©2015 Great Minds. eureka-math.org
G2-M1-HWH-1.3.0-07.2015

11

G2-M8-Lesson 10

> I know that these shapes show halves because each shape has 2 equal shares.

1. Do the shapes below show halves or thirds? _halves_

 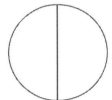 

Draw 1 more line to partition each shape into fourths.

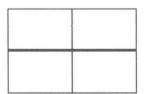  

> I can partition this shape into fourths by drawing another diagonal line from the opposite corners. That way, there are 4 equal shares!

2. Partition each rectangle into fourths. Then, shade the shapes as indicated.

 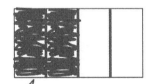 

      4 fourths   2 fourths   1 fourth

> I shade all four to show 4 fourths. 4 fourths is the same as 1 whole!

> I can show 2 fourths by shading two parts.

> To show 1 fourth, I just shade 1 part!

    Lesson 10:   Partition circles and rectangles into equal parts, and describe those parts as halves, thirds, or fourths.

3. Split the granola bar below so that Lisa, MJ, and Jessa all have an equal share. Label each student's share with her name.

Lisa	MJ	Jessa

What fraction of the granola bar did the girls get in all?

3 thirds

They shared the whole granola bar! That is 3 thirds!

I split the bar into 3 equal shares because there are 3 people eating it!

EUREKA MATH™   **Lesson 10:**   Partition circles and rectangles into equal parts, and describe those parts as halves, thirds, or fourths.   13

©2015 Great Minds. eureka-math.org
G2-M1-HWH-1.3.0-07.2015

G2-M8-Lesson 11

1. For part (a), identify the shaded area.
   a.

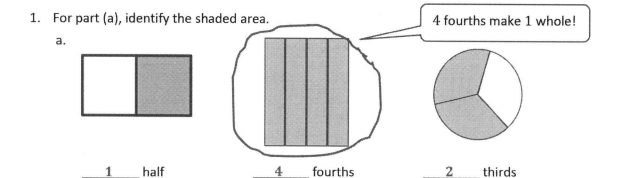

   4 fourths make 1 whole!

   ___1___ half   ___4___ fourths   ___2___ thirds

   b. Circle the shape above that has a shaded area that shows 1 whole.

2. What fraction do you need to color so that 1 whole is shaded?
   a.   b.

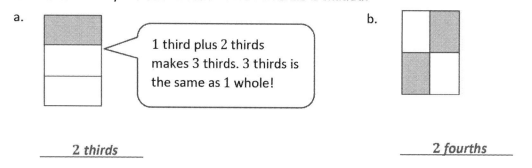

   1 third plus 2 thirds
   makes 3 thirds. 3 thirds is
   the same as 1 whole!

   ___2 thirds___   ___2 fourths___

3. Complete the drawing to show 1 whole.

   This is 1 third.

   Draw 1 whole.

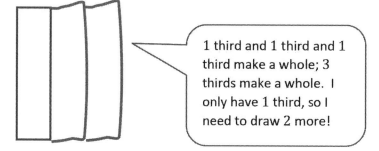

   1 third and 1 third and 1
   third make a whole; 3
   thirds make a whole. I
   only have 1 third, so I
   need to draw 2 more!

Lesson 11:   Describe a whole by the number of equal parts including 2 halves, 3
                            thirds, and 4 fourths.

                    ©2015 Great Minds. eureka-math.org
                    G2-M1-HWH-1.3.0-07.2015

EUREKA MATH

G2-M8-Lesson 12

1. Partition the rectangles in 2 different ways to show equal shares.

    2 halves

> Look, I can show thirds as long, skinny rectangles or short, fat rectangles!
> They don't need to have the same shape to cover the same amount of space.

    3 thirds

> I can show fourths in more than one way! As long as the 4 parts cover
> the same amount of space they are equal, so I have made fourths!

    4 fourths

2. Cut out the rectangle.

   a. Cut the rectangle in half to make 2 equal size rectangles. Shade 1 half using your pencil.

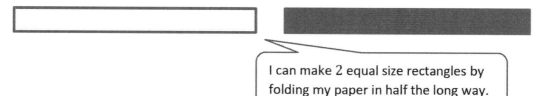

   I can make 2 equal size rectangles by folding my paper in half the long way.

   b. Rearrange the halves to create a new rectangle with no gaps or overlaps.

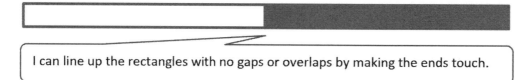

   I can line up the rectangles with no gaps or overlaps by making the ends touch.

   c. Cut each equal part in half to make 4 equal size rectangles.

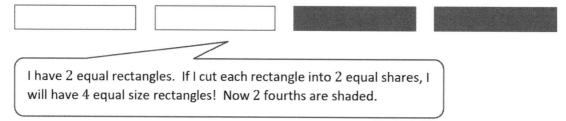

   I have 2 equal rectangles. If I cut each rectangle into 2 equal shares, I will have 4 equal size rectangles! Now 2 fourths are shaded.

   d. Rearrange the new equal shares to create different polygons.

   e. Draw one of your new polygons from part (d) below. One half is shaded!

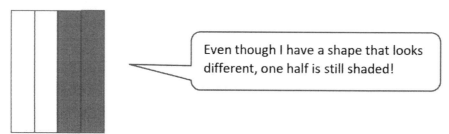

   Even though I have a shape that looks different, one half is still shaded!

Lesson 12:   Recognize that equal parts of an identical rectangle can have different shapes.

G2-M8-Lesson 13

1. Tell what fraction of each clock is shaded in the space below using the words *quarter, quarters, half,* or *halves*.

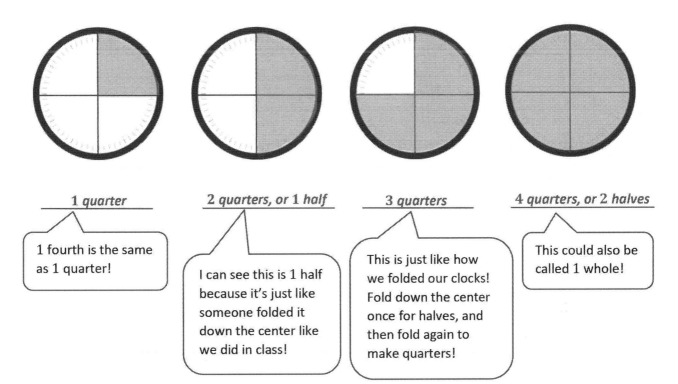

___1 *quarter*___

> 1 fourth is the same as 1 quarter!

___2 *quarters*, or 1 *half*___

> I can see this is 1 half because it's just like someone folded it down the center like we did in class!

___3 *quarters*___

> This is just like how we folded our clocks! Fold down the center once for halves, and then fold again to make quarters!

___4 *quarters*, or 2 *halves*___

> This could also be called 1 whole!

2. Write the time shown on each clock.

a.

_____9:30_____

When the minute hand points to the 6, I skip count by 5's up to 30. So I can say 9:30, or I can say half past 9 since the minute hand has moved halfway around the clock!

b.

_____6:15_____

I know that a fourth of the hour has passed. That's 1 quarter!

3. Draw the minute hand on the clock to show the correct time.

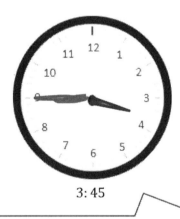

3:45

I remember that 1 quarter is 15 minutes, 2 quarters is 30 minutes, and 3 quarters is 45 minutes. 3 quarters of the way around the clock will be at the 9.

11:30

30 minutes is halfway around the clock, or half past the hour. Halfway around the clock is at the 6.

EUREKA MATH

G2-M8-Lesson 14

1. Fill in the missing numbers.

    60, 55, 50, _45_, 40, _35_, _30_, _25_, _20_, _15_, _10_, _5_, _0_

    > I skip-count back by 5's. It's just like counting back around the clock!

2. Draw the hour and minute hands on the clocks to match the correct time.

3:05

> I know that since it is only 5 minutes past the hour, the hour hand should be pointing at the 3.

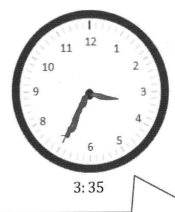

3:35

> More than half of the hour has passed, so the hour hand should be pointing about halfway between the 3 and 4. I know that when the minute hand is pointing to the 6, it is 30 minutes past the hour. When it's pointing to the 7, I add on 5 minutes, so the clock shows 3:35.

6:55

> Since it's 6:55, that means it is almost 7. The hour hand should be pointing right before the 7 since it's just 5 minutes before 7 o'clock.

G2-M8-Lesson 15

1. Decide whether the activity below would happen in the a.m. or the p.m. Circle your answer.

Waking up for school   (a.m.)/ p.m.

Eating dinner   a.m. /(p.m.)

Reading a bedtime story   a.m. /(p.m.)

Making breakfast   (a.m.)/ p.m.

> *A* comes before *P* in the alphabet. That's how I remember that a.m. is morning and p.m. is afternoon. The morning comes before the afternoon!

2. What time does the clock show?

   __3__ : __55__

   > Even though it looks like the hour hand is pointing to the 4, I know it's not 4 o'clock yet because the minute hand shows 55 minutes! I have to wait 5 more minutes!

3. Draw the hands on the analog clock to match the time on the digital clock. Then, circle a.m. or p.m. based on the description given.

   Brushing your teeth after you wake up

   7 : 10   (a.m.) or p.m.

   > I know it's a.m. because it says "after you wake up," and that happens in the morning!

   > The digital time shows the digits of the hour and the minutes. On the analog clock, the little hand points to the 7 to show the hour. For the minute hand, I can count by 5's to figure out how to show 10 minutes after the hour.
   > 5, 10...so the big hand points to the 2 to show 10 minutes.

4. Write what you might be doing if it were a.m. or p.m.

   a.m. ___*eating breakfast*___

   p.m. ___*reading a book*___

   > Usually at 7 in the morning, I am eating breakfast. 7 p.m. is 1 hour before bed, and that's the time I read!

Lesson 15:   Tell time to the nearest five minutes; relate *a.m.* and *p.m.* to time of day.

G2-M8-Lesson 16

1. How much time has passed?

> 6:30 is half past the hour. That means that it takes another half to get to the next hour, so 30 minutes have passed.

6:30 a.m. → 7:00 a.m.   _30 minutes_

4:00 p.m. → 9:00 p.m.   _5 hours_

> I can add on from 4:00 p.m. to get to 9:00 p.m. 4 + 5 = 9, so 5 hours have passed.

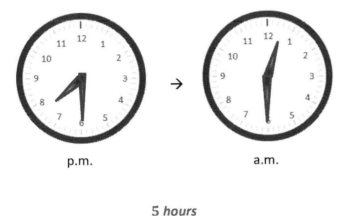

p.m.   a.m.

5 hours

> This is tricky because the time changes from p.m. to a.m., but I know that p.m. turns to a.m. at 12.
>
> I see that the minute hand is in the same place on both clocks, so all I need to do is count up from 7 to 12. 7 + 5 = 12, so, from 7:30 p.m. to 12:30 a.m., 5 hours have passed.

2. Anna spent 3 hours at dance practice. She finished at 6:15 p.m. What time did she start?

? —— + 3 hours ——→ 6:15

> I can use the arrow way with hours and minutes to make solving easier.

6 − 3 = 3, so 6:15 minus 3 hours is 3:15.

Anna started at 3:15.